ELEMENTS OF GRADUATION

PRINCIPAL CONTRIBUTOR

MORTON D. MILLER

ASSOCIATE CONTRIBUTORS

HENRY S. BEERS   CHARLES A. SPOERL

HUGH H. WOLFENDEN

PUBLISHED BY

THE ACTUARIAL SOCIETY OF AMERICA

AMERICAN INSTITUTE OF ACTUARIES

1946

Printed in U. S. A. by the Franklin Printing Company, Philadelphia, Penna.

PREFACE

The Actuarial Society of America and the American Institute of Actuaries propose to issue jointly a series of monographs on subjects required in the Syllabus of Examinations.

This Monograph on Elements of Graduation is the first of the series. The principal contributor is Mr. Morton D. Miller, who is primarily responsible for the matter included and the views expressed. He was assisted by the following associate contributors: Messrs. H. S. Beers, C. A. Spoerl, and H. H. Wolfenden.

The thanks of the Society, the Institute and the Joint Committee are due to all the contributors who have freely given of their time and labor, with the sole purpose of helping others—especially students.

The Monograph was first reproduced by the photo-offset process and published in 1946 under the auspices of the Joint Committee on Actuarial Studies, constituted as follows:

For the Society	*For the Institute*
ALDEN T. BUNYAN	HENRY S. BEERS
RICHARD C. GUEST	JOHN D. BUCHANAN
SAMUEL MILLIGAN	F. BRUCE GERHARD
HUGH H. WOLFENDEN	EDWARD H. WELLS

E. M. McCONNEY, *Chairman*

It is now being brought out in printed form by the Joint Education and Examination Committee. This Committee, including the Operating Committee for Part 5, is as follows:

JOINT EDUCATION AND EXAMINATION COMMITTEE

JAMES R. HERMAN, *General Chairman*
F. BRUCE GERHARD, *Education Chairman*
CHARLES A. SPOERL, *Examination Chairman*
HAROLD R. LAWSON, *Vice-Chairman for Readings*
MORTON D. MILLER, *Vice-Chairman for Panel Notes*
ROBERT P. COATES, *Vice-Chairman for Examinations*

BERT A. WINTER, *Chairman*, PART 5

RICHARD D. BALDWIN	JOHN F. RYAN
JAMES H. BRADDOCK	ROBERT E. SHALEN
PAUL K. FRAZER	MORTIMER SPIEGELMAN

iii

TABLE OF CONTENTS

v

TABLE OF FIGURES

ELEMENTS OF GRADUATION

CHAPTER ONE

Introduction

1.0 The actuary is concerned with the contingencies of death, disability, retirement, sickness, withdrawal, marriage, etc. He must know the probabilities or rates of occurrence of such events in order to predict their future occurrence and in order to be able to calculate premiums, reserves, annuities, and so forth, for insurance and other financial operations. Tables setting forth such probabilities must be constructed, and for that purpose observations are made of the happening of such events. Graduation is one of the steps in the construction of these tables. In this monograph we shall consider:

(*a*) How the problem of graduation arises;

(*b*) What the process of graduation means;

(*c*) What the justifications for the process of graduation are;

(*d*) How the graduation of an observed series may be accomplished;

(*e*) What the criteria of an acceptable graduation are.

For the sake of simplicity, our discussions will mainly be of mortality tables and rates of mortality, often without referring to other tables or contingencies. The extension of the ideas to other contingencies and to other types of statistics generally will be apparent and should be kept in mind.

1.1 *How the problem of graduation arises.*

The problem of graduation arises in connection with the construction of mortality tables because a series of observed mortality rates will be found to contain irregularities which we have reason to believe are not a feature of the true, underlying rates of mortality. Since no law of mortality, in the sense of a physical law, is known to us, nor is one likely to be discovered, we have no way of knowing *a priori* what the basic pattern of mortality is.

1

We must therefore rely on the information supplied by observations of the rates of mortality actually being experienced.

In the construction of a mortality table, a number of insured individuals (or policies, or amounts of insurance, as the case may be) exposed to the risk of death are observed over a period of time. The data are assembled and classified through the application of appropriate methods not considered in this monograph, leading to a tabulation of the actual deaths and exposures at each age or sometimes in each age group. In this monograph the number (or amount) of actual or observed deaths occurring during the year of age from x to $x+1$ will be denoted by Θ''_x, and the corresponding number (or amount) exposed to risk of death by E_x. The actual or observed rate of mortality, often called the crude rate of mortality, will be denoted by $q''_x = \Theta''_x / E_x$. The graduated rate of mortality will be denoted by q_x, and the expected deaths by the graduated table will be denoted by $\Theta_x = q_x E_x$. The problem of graduation begins after the observed rates of mortality have been obtained.

It should be noted that in any one investigation all the lives being observed are assumed to have, for all practical purposes, the same basic pattern of mortality, for the inclusion of non-homogeneous elements might invalidate the results by the introduction of spurious variations. For instance, because their patterns of mortality are essentially different, the class of substandard issues and the class of policies continued under non-forfeiture options are usually treated separately from the larger class of standard lives.

It is clear, of course, that in dealing with so complex a matter as mortality, which varies by sex, occupation, habitat, nationality, marital status and so on, as well as by age, it is not possible to procure truly homogeneous data without so reducing the volume of the data as to make them of little worth. Consequently, a practical view of the question of homogeneity must be taken. Nonetheless, in order that the results be reliable, it is important that the data be homogeneous as far as practicable and that observed irregularities be not ascribable to any large extent to defects inherent in the material observed. In what follows, not only are the data assumed to be substantially homogeneous before they are considered for graduation, but errors of reporting, such as the systematic over-statement of older ages present in population material, are supposed to have been corrected.

Despite the elimination of factors which might in themselves introduce irregularities, a series of observed mortality rates always remains irregular. This fact may be brought out from an inspection of the series and its differences, but will appear more clearly, as illustrated in Figure 1, if the observed values are plotted and joined by straight line segments. The general progression of the rates of mortality will be found to be somewhat obscured by the irregularities characteristic of such observations.

Diagram Illustrating Effect of Graduation

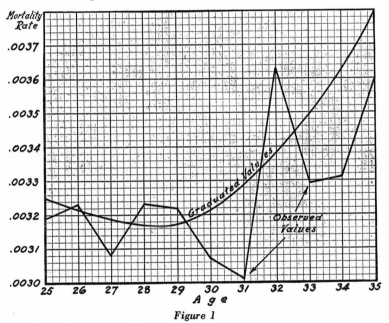

Figure 1

It is with irregular series of observed values of continuously varying quantities, such as mortality rates, that the problem of graduation deals. The process of graduation is applied in order to obtain an adequate representation of the basic pattern which the variable under consideration is believed to follow.

As has been suggested, the problem of graduation is by no means peculiar to actuarial work. The irregularities present in a series of observed mortality rates are characteristic of observations made in connection with continuously varying quantities in other fields of knowledge. Accordingly, the sociologist, biologist or physicist may also have to employ the process of graduation to bring out the underlying pattern of variation of a variable he is investigating, which is obscured by the irregularities of observation.

1.2 *What the process of graduation means.*

For reasons that will be discussed in (1.4), the underlying curve of mortality is assumed to be smooth, regular and continuous. Graduation may then be defined as the process of securing from an irregular series of observed values of a continuous variable a smooth regular series of values consistent in a general way with the observed series of values. This smooth series, or series of graduated values, is then taken as a representation of the underlying law which gave rise to the series of observed values.

Thus, in graduating a series of $\omega+1$ observed mortality rates from q_0'' to q_ω'', the graduation process will substitute $\omega+1$ graduated mortality rates, q_0 to q_ω, lying close to the crude values but larger at some ages and smaller at others. These graduated rates are obtained by altering each observed rate by reference to the other observed rates so that the new series will be smooth rather than irregular but at the same time will exhibit the trend indicated by the observed series.

A series of observed values, u_x'', may be thought of as having two components. The first is the underlying smooth regular series, V_x, free from the fluctuations characteristic of observed data. The second is a superimposed irregular series, e_x, consisting of a haphazard array of positive and negative terms which account for the irregularities appearing in the observed u_x'' series. If we write $u_x'' = V_x + e_x$, and if G be a graduation process applied to u_x'' to obtain the graduated series, u_x, we may then write, symbolically,

$$G(u_x'') = G(V_x) + G(e_x) = u_x. \tag{1.21}$$

Since any graduation process operates on both the V_x and e_x components, it should be such that its application will effect a redistribution and reduction of the e_x series, permitting positive and negative errors to offset one another, while it leaves the V_x series substantially unchanged.

It is too much to anticipate that graduation will be successful in wholly eliminating the error component of the observed series.

Consequently, the graduated series u_x will contain an element of residual error and must therefore be thought of as a representation of the underlying law rather than as the law itself. This distinction will usually be of theoretical rather than practical importance.

1.3 *Smoothness and fit.*

Graduation is characterized by two essential qualities; (i) smoothness and (ii) fit, or consistency with the observed data. The graduated series should be smooth as compared with the ungraduated series, but it should be consistent with the indications of the ungraduated series.

Smoothness and fit are not independent of one another. Since in smoothing an observed series its values must be changed, the new values will be made to depart from the observed series. Generally, an increase in the smoothing results in a reduction in the fit. Conversely, when the graduated series is drawn closer to the observed series, improving the fit, smoothness usually suffers. The ultimate of fit lies in the exact reproduction of the observed series with no attendant smoothing whatsoever, i.e., no graduation at all.

The two qualities are, therefore, basically inconsistent in the sense that smoothness may not be improved beyond a certain point without some sacrifice of closeness of fit, and vice versa. As a result, any graduated series must of necessity follow a middle course between optimum fit and optimum smoothness; it must represent the result of a compromise between the two. To be of general use, a graduation method must allow the graduator some latitude in choosing the relative emphasis to place on smoothness and fit in the graduated series.

No one method can at the same time accomplish a maximum of both smoothness and fit. All methods control, or permit the control of, the relative emphasis to be placed on smoothness and fit, although each method will be found to do so in a different way. In the application of a method to a specific problem, the circumstances of that problem dictate the nature and extent of the compromise to be effected between fit and smoothness.

1.4 *What the justifications for the process of graduation are.*

In defining the process of graduation, we postulated a smooth, regular underlying series of true values corresponding to the irregular series of observed values. The theoretical reasons justifying graduations are those upon which this assumption rests.

We have reason to believe that most of the laws of nature do not exhibit irregular variations or sharp breaks, but may be expressed in terms of regular and continuous functions. This conclusion, which the scientific pioneers reached on intuitive grounds alone, is adequately supported by experiment. Nevertheless, any set of actual observations of a series of measurements corresponding to a physical law will exhibit irregularities; some will be positive, some negative. The irregularities will be greater in some sets of observations than in others, but our experience with many sets of observations indicates that, as the data are increased, the irregularities tend to become less important. If it were possible to secure unlimited data, it is believed that the irregularities would become insignificant.

The mathematical theory of probability deals with the reasons for this behavior. According to this theory, even though the true rates of mortality were known *a priori*, the observed rates of mortality given by dividing the number exposed to risk into the actual deaths at each age would differ from those called for by the law of mortality and would comprise an irregular series. The irregularities, often referred to as errors of observation, or as chance fluctuations, arise because of the limited, necessarily finite extent of the observations.

Of course, we do not know the true rates of mortality, and since a law of mortality will probably never be discovered, they will in all likelihood never be known. We have only the series of observed probabilities given by our limited observations, from which we must estimate the unknown true mortality rates. Viewed in this way, the problem of graduation is a mathematical problem in which we are asked to estimate, or secure a representation of, the series of true rates of mortality that is assumed to have given rise to the irregular series of observed probabilities.

Besides the reasons set forth above, there is an obvious practical justification for the process of graduation. The actuary expects to use his tables of mortality for the calculation of premiums, reserve factors, annuities, and so forth. There is nothing to be gained by assuming that mortality varies other than regularly and continuously. Capricious irregularities in the tables from age to age disturbing the orderly progression of premiums, etc., would be inconsistent with the common sense view that such figures should be reasonably regular, and would tend to arouse an entirely justifiable skepticism.

1.5 *How the graduation of an observed series may be accomplished.*

Several means have been developed by which the graduation of an observed series may be accomplished and the problem of graduation solved. These methods may be classified as follows and will be discussed in some detail in succeeding chapters:

(i) The Graphic Method: In this method, the observed values are suitably plotted on graph paper and among them a smooth, continuous curve is drawn as the basis of the graduated series.

(ii) The Interpolation Method: In this method, the data are combined into age groups and the graduated series is obtained by interpolation between points determined as representative of the groups.

(iii) The Adjusted-Average Method: In this method, each term of the graduated series is a weighted average of a fixed number of terms of the observed series to which it is central.

(iv) The Difference-Equation Method: In this method, the graduated series is determined by a difference equation derived from an analytic measure of the relative emphasis to be placed upon fit and smoothness.

(v) Graduation by Mathematical Formula: In this method, the graduated series is represented by a mathematical curve fitted to the data.

1.6 *The acceptability of a graduation.*

When a graduation has been made, the graduator's task is not complete. Each graduation must be tested as to its acceptability.

As distinguished from the more familiar mathematical problems, graduation does not have a single numerical solution. Depending upon the choice of method, upon the proportions in which fit and smoothness are combined in the instance, and upon the skill and experience of the graduator, different numerical values will be obtained for the graduated series.

How, then, are we to determine whether a completed graduation is to be accepted as satisfactory and whether one graduation is preferable to another? The criteria must be based on the consideration and measurement of the two qualities (i) smoothness and (ii) fit. The quantitative tests of the acceptability of the results of any graduation may be considered under these two heads.

1.7 *Tests of smoothness.*

The function in which we are interested should exhibit a smooth and continuous progression from term to term. The tests of smoothness are, therefore, customarily applied to the graduated rates of mortality.

Smoothness is tested by inspecting the progression and size of some order or orders of the finite differences of the graduated q_x's. The progression of the differences is reviewed by computing, say, the second, third, and fourth differences and observing the extent of their regularity from age to age.

The usual numerical measures of the size of the differences are based on third differences. They are:

(a) $\Sigma(\Delta^3 q_x)^2$, the sum of the squares of the
3rd differences, or alternatively,

(b) $\Sigma|\Delta^3 q_x|$, the sum of their absolute values.

The smaller such sums, the smoother the graduation is adjudged to be. Ordinarily, the differences are taken over unit intervals, but where rounding errors may have a material effect, differences over intervals of two or five units may also be compared.

The numerical measures of smoothness are more in the nature of comparative than absolute tests, facilitating the comparison between two or more graduations of the same data. In the case of a single graduation, the tests of smoothness are consequently limited to a consideration of the progression of the differences of several orders.

When a graduation is performed by the fitting of a mathematical curve, e.g., a Makeham curve, the graduated series has the inherent smoothness of a mathematical curve and is almost invariably considered satisfactory as to smoothness without invoking any test.

1.8 *Tests of fit.*

The tests of fit are commonly applied to the deaths. The deaths expected by the table of graduated mortality rates applied to the actual exposures (or simply the expected deaths) are compared with the actual or observed deaths. The usual tests deal with the differences between the actual deaths and the expected deaths, $\theta''_x - \theta_x$, otherwise referred to as the deviations. When exposures are not available, the tests are applied directly to the differences between the graduated and ungraduated values of q_x.

Because the observations at some points include more data than at others, they are more reliable, and we say that they have

more weight or greater relative significance. Accordingly, it is at
the points of greater weight, i.e., the ages where the exposures are
larger, that a closer fit between the graduated and ungraduated
mortality rates is to be sought. Since the product of a mortality
rate by the corresponding exposed to risk equals a number of
deaths, this fact is automatically taken into account, and allowance
made for the weight of the observations at each age, by applying
tests of fit to the deaths in lieu of the mortality rates, themselves.

As illustrated in Figure 1, the graduated values should lie among
the ungraduated values and the graduated series should inter-
twine with the ungraduated series. A satisfactory fit should, therefore, exist throughout the table. In order to establish that fact, the
tests of fit should be applied to sub-groups of the data as well as to
the entire series.

A number of different tests of fit, of varying degrees of com-
plexity, are available. All of them would not necessarily be applied
to any one graduation. The extent of the testing and the com-
plexity of the tests used depends upon the purpose for which the
graduated table is intended as well as the volume of the observed
data. Two of the simpler tests based upon the deaths are described
in the following paragraphs (a) and (b) and a test of a different
nature in paragraph (c).

(a) The sum of the deviations, $\Sigma(\Theta''_x - \Theta_x)$, and their first
moment, $\Sigma x(\Theta''_x - \Theta_x)$, should be close to zero, which is their
expected or average value in accordance with the mathematical
theory of probability. In other words, the total of the expected
deaths should be nearly equal to the total of the actual deaths, and
the average age at death by the graduated table should correspond
closely to the average age at death computed from the data.

This test is made in practice by calculating from the column of
deviations a column of accumulated deviations, each term of
which consists of a sub-total of the deviations up to that point.
The sum of the deviations and the sum of the column of sub-
totals should be close to zero. This is mathematically equivalent
to the requirement that the sum and the first moment of the deviations be close to zero.

(b) The number of alternations in the signs of the deviations
and of the accumulated deviations and the pattern of such signs
is also a measure of the closeness of fit of a graduation.

Having in mind the interlacing of the graduated and ungraduated series, frequent changes in the signs of the deviations should be exhibited and long runs of the same sign should be investigated. A series of the same signs in the deviations indicates that in that area the curves of the graduated and ungraduated series lie wholly above or below one another and that some feature of the data may have been slighted by the graduation.

For a series of n terms, the expected number of changes of sign in the deviations is approximately $\frac{n-1}{2}$. That is, if a graduation exhibits about the same number of changes in sign as continuances in sign, in the column of deviations, the graduation is considered satisfactory in this respect. To insure closeness of fit throughout the whole series, the accumulated deviations should also show fairly frequent changes in sign.

(c) A comparison of the values of financial functions is sometimes used in connection with important tables. Annuity values or premiums are calculated by using the graduated mortality rates and compared with those based on the observed mortality rates. Since the computation of these functions involves some graduation because errors present at successive ages are permitted to offset one another to a certain extent, the standard of acceptability of the fit should be more stringent than for a test applied directly to a table of q_x's.

1.81 *Improving the fit.*

If, in a particular graduation, the totals of the deviations and of the accumulated deviations are not considered small enough, the fit can be improved by a simple transformation of the series of the graduated mortality rates, q_x, to obtain a better series, q'_x. An excellent method is to set

$$q'_x = aq_x + b \qquad (1.811)$$

and then determine a and b so as to make the total of the deviations and of the accumulated deviations vanish.

If the expected deaths by the first graduation are Θ_x, and if $\Sigma^2\Theta_x$ is taken to mean the total of the accumulated deaths, a and b are to be calculated from the following pair of simultaneous equations:

$$\begin{aligned}
\Sigma E_x q'_x = \Sigma \Theta''_x &= a\Sigma\Theta_x + b\Sigma E_x, \\
\Sigma^2 E_x q'_x = \Sigma^2\Theta''_x &= a\Sigma^2\Theta_x + b\Sigma^2 E_x.
\end{aligned} \qquad (1.812)$$

When the numerical values of a and b have been computed, the revised mortality rates may be calculated by (1.811). The rounding of the values to a limited number of significant figures will prevent the deviations and accumulated deviations from coming out precisely zero, except by coincidence.

When there is only a handful of data to be graduated, this process may be used in lieu of making a formal graduation. The q_x's may be taken from some appropriate existing standard table; then when a and b have been determined by equations (1.812), the q'_x's computed by (1.811) become the graduated series.

1.9 *Exercises.*

1.91 How does the problem of graduation arise in actuarial work?

1.92 What is meant by graduation? What two factors are involved? Discuss their relationship.

1.93 What are the justifications for graduation?

1.94 Describe briefly the criteria which are used in determining whether a graduation is satisfactory.

1.95 The table below shows the exposed to risk, actual claims, and ungraduated mortality rates for ages 70-84, inclusive, together with the results of two graduations. Compare these graduations by applying tests of smoothness and fit to them.

Age	Exposed to Risk	Actual Deaths	Ungraduated Mortality Rate	Graduation I		Graduation II	
				Mortality Rate	Expected Claims	Mortality Rate	Expected Claims
70	135	6	.044	.0591	8.0	.0471	6.4
71	143	12	.084	.0646	9.2	.0530	7.6
72	140	10	.071	.0704	9.9	.0602	8.4
73	144	11	.076	.0768	11.1	.0690	9.9
74	149	6	.040	.0837	12.5	.0792	11.8
75	154	16	.104	.0913	14.1	.0904	13.9
76	150	24	.160	.0994	14.9	.1020	15.3
77	139	8	.058	.1084	15.1	.1138	15.8
78	145	16	.110	.1180	17.1	.1261	18.3
79	140	13	.093	.1284	18.0	.1387	19.4
80	137	19	.139	.1398	19.2	.1516	20.8
81	136	21	.154	.1518	20.6	.1647	22.4
82	126	23	.183	.1649	20.8	.1779	22.4
83	126	26	.206	.1791	22.6	.1910	24.1
84	109	26	.239	.1944	21.2	.2041	22.2
	2,073	237			234.3		238.7

1.96 Apply the procedure described in (1.81) to one of the graduations given in (1.95).

CHAPTER TWO

The Graphic Method

2.0 The graphic method, which arises naturally out of the diagrammatic presentation of facts, was the first to be developed. The method was applied by Joshua Milne, actuary of the Sun Life Office, London, in the graduation of one of the earliest mortality tables, the Carlisle Table of Mortality, published in 1815. The data consisted of census populations and death registers in two parishes in Carlisle. The graduation was performed separately on the population and deaths arranged in quinquennial and decennial age groups.

2.1 *The graphic method.*

In the graphic method, the observed values are suitably plotted on graph paper and among them a smooth, continuous curve is drawn as the basis of the graduated series. The steps required by the method may be set down as follows:

  (i) Grouping the data, unless the data are already grouped;
  (ii) The selection of graph paper of appropriate form and ruling, and the determination of a proper scale;
  (iii) Plotting the observed values, together with some indication of their relative weights if this information is available;
  (iv) Drawing a smooth, continuous curve among the observed values, free hand or with mechanical aids;
  (v) Reading the graduated values from the diagram;
  (vi) Adjusting to improve smoothness and fit.

2.2 *Grouping.*

Unless the data are very extensive, the greater fluctuations likely to be present at individual ages as well as the large number of observed points for individual ages may serve to confuse the graduator and to conceal the indications of the data. Consequently, an almost necessary part of the application of the graphic method is the combination of the data into groups of suitable size, if they are not already so grouped.

Grouping performs a graduating function. By the combination of the data, the irregularities or errors within each group are permitted to offset one another. A series of grouped values will therefore be a smoother, more regular series than the observed series of individual values and will, of course, be consistent with the observed series. Each of the grouped values assumes greater weight than any of the individual observations comprising the group, and the underlying pattern of variation is more definitely revealed.

The number of ages in each group may be equal or may be permitted to vary, but the number of groups should neither be so many as to exhibit extreme fluctuations nor so few as to eliminate some important feature of the data or furnish insufficient points for graduation. In practice, some experimentation may be necessary to decide upon the most suitable grouping of the data.

The question of where to locate each group point arises. If a review of the data shows that it is not materially contrary to the facts to place the points at the middle of the group intervals, that simple course may be followed. If such is not the case, or if a more refined method is desired, the assistance of a standard table with rates of mortality thought to be somewhat similar to those of the given experience may be employed and account taken of the weight of the observations at individual ages. The deaths expected by the standard table applied to the exposures are first calculated at each age; then the total of such expected deaths is divided by the corresponding total exposure so as to determine a standard-table average death rate for each group. Next, the precise fractional age which corresponds to each such rate is computed from the standard table. Finally, the average observed mortality rate for each age group is located within its group interval at the fractional age calculated for the interval.

2.3 *Plotting.*

When the observed values are plotted, it is important to indicate in some fashion the points which should carry greater weight when it comes to selecting the curve of graduated values. One very simple method is to write the exposed to risk near the points. A more helpful system is to compute the standard deviation, σ_x, corresponding to each exposure and observed rate of mortality, working to one or two significant figures. If the exposure is by lives,

$$\sigma_x = \sqrt{\frac{q_x''(1-q_x'')}{E_x}}. \tag{2.31}$$

Then, as each point is plotted, another pair of points, distant σ_x above and below the data point, are indicated as well. These two extra points are joined by a heavy line. In drawing the curve of graduated values, the draftsman keeps in mind that there is about one chance in three that a graduated value lies outside the σ_x pair of points. If he draws the curve so that it intersects about two out of three of the heavy lines, he may feel assured that his graduation is likely to be successful. In practice, since $(1-q_x)$ is very close to one, (2.31) may be approximated by $q_x'' \div \sqrt{\Theta_x''}$. The corresponding approximation for a mortality ratio is M.R. $\div \sqrt{\Theta_x''}$.

If this method is used, it may not be necessary to do any preliminary grouping.

2.4 *Mechanical aids.*

Graph papers are available in many different sizes and scales. In addition, there are a number of special graph papers which serve to make the method more easily and more widely applicable. The paper called semi-logarithmic (Figure 4 on page 48) is particularly useful for the direct graduation of mortality rates. It has the conventional vertical rulings but the horizontal rulings are spaced in proportion to the logarithms of the numbers appearing on the vertical scale. Thus, the width of the section from 1 to 10 is the same as the one from 10 to 100, or from 100 to 1,000.

The freehand drawing of a smooth, continuous curve is by no means easy. Several mechanical devices are available, however, for the assistance of the graduator. The graduator may have the help of a French curve or may use a spline and weights, both of which are pictured in Figure 2. A spline is a flexible rod of metal or other composition made for this purpose. It is bent into position over the data in the shape of the graduated curve and held in place by weights fitting into a groove cut into the side. The graduated curve is then drawn along the edge of the spline. There are also "flexible rules" and "adjustable curves."

2.5 *Reading the graph and adjusting to improve smoothness and fit.*

One of the problems often experienced in using the graphic method is the difficulty of reading the graduated values accurately from the graph. In the case of mortality rates, this is aggravated by the relatively wide range of values present—roughly from .001 to 1.000. If the scale is large enough to permit accurate reading of one section of the curve, it may be so large that in another portion the curve crosses the lines representing the ordinates at a very acute angle, thus not only increasing the difficulty of reading the graph but multiplying greatly the effect on the graduated values of a slight deflection of the curve. Sometimes legibility may be improved by choosing different scales for different sections of the table. It is also possible to reduce the range of variation by graduating a suitable function of q_x such as $\log (q_x + .1)$ rather than q_x itself.

Figure 2a—French Curve

Figure 2b—Spline and Weights

The smoothness of the graduated series may be considerably improved by making small adjustments in the graduated values. This is usually done by working with the column of second differences. It should be noted that a change of $+h$ in the value of one member of a graduated series changes 3 adjacent second differences by $+h, -2h, +h$. Similarly, a change of $+h, +h$ in two successive values changes 4 adjacent second differences by $+h$, $-h$, $-h$, $+h$. These and other similar relationships may be used to improve the smoothness of the column of second differences, without involving any major changes in the graduated series itself.

When really smooth graduated values are desired, it is always possible to make a subsequent graduation by some mathematical method of the values read off from the graph. These methods are treated in detail in later chapters. Even when this refinement is not considered necessary, it is usually a good plan to improve the fit by adjusting the graduated rates by the process described in (1.81).

2.6 *Graduation with reference to a standard table.*

Another technique has distinct advantages. A standard existing table may be selected and the ratios of the observed q_x's to those of the standard table may be computed and graduated in lieu of graduating the mortality rates. Afterward, the graduated q_x's may be calculated from the standard table by multiplying by the graduated ratios. Not only does this procedure reduce the range of variation of the series being graduated but it also may establish a useful relationship between the observed data and the existing standard table. The table chosen as a standard should be such that the pattern of its rates of mortality is similar to that of the given experience; a table graduated by a mathematical formula is to be preferred because of its smoothness.

Care should be taken to test the smoothness of the graduated mortality rates rather than of the ratios. The progression of the series of q_x's should be reviewed by an inspection of its differences to be sure that the q_x's or their first or second differences do not show inadmissible variations, e.g., a run of negative second differences at a place in the series where one is satisfied that the basic series of true mortality rates would show consistently positive values. Such variations might not be apparent from an inspection of the ratios to the standard table alone.

2.7 *Exercises.*

2.71 Graduate graphically the ratios of actual to expected mortality shown in the data of (9.1). Compare the second and third differences of the graduated and ungraduated ratios. Calculate the graduated deaths, the deviations between the actual and graduated deaths and their sum, and the column of accumulated deviations and its sum. Notice the number of changes of sign in the deviations and in the accumulated deviations.

2.72 You are given the number exposed and the number of deaths at each age in a mortality investigation among pensioners. There are approximately 500 deaths in the experience. Describe in detail how you would obtain a graduated mortality table from these figures, using the graphic method and making use of the Combined Annuity Mortality Table as giving the general shape of the underlying curve.

2.73 Describe a method suitable for use in graduating a mortality experience in which the exposures and deaths, available at individual ages, are rather scanty.

CHAPTER THREE

The Interpolation Method

3.0 The interpolation method was the first graduation method developed subsequent to the graphic method. It was evolved primarily in connection with population statistics where it has been extensively used. Nevertheless, the method is by no means limited to population material and may be applied to insurance and other data.

3.1 *The interpolation method.*

Under the interpolation method, the graduated series is obtained by interpolating between special points determined as representative of the age groups into which the data are combined. Since graduation involves the replacement of an irregular observed series by a regular smooth series consistent with the trend of the observed values, clearly the interpolation method of graduation includes more than interpolation alone. As a graduation process, the interpolation method comprises three elements:

  (i) The grouping of the data;
 (ii) The securing of a smooth, reliable series of points, one for each group, representative of the data;
(iii) The computation of graduated values by interpolation based upon these points.

3.2 *Grouping.*

The first step in the interpolation method is the combination of the data into groups of suitable size and number. As discussed in (2.2), a graduating function is performed by this grouping. This is true whether the data are given already grouped, as is often the case, or are put into groups by the combination of data at individual ages.

In the case of population statistics, the data are usually quite extensive so that grouping would not be resorted to just to reduce the errors of observation. Still, errors of reporting evidenced by a heaping of the data at specific ages are commonly present. Such errors are of a different type from errors of observation; they tend to introduce a systematic bias. The data are grouped in the hope that by distributing the excess population over the neighboring ages the effects of these errors of reporting will be eliminated or greatly reduced. To that end, an effort is made to select the particular grouping that will best compensate for the heaping of the data.

3.3 *Pivotal points.*

The second step in the application of the method is the calculation of the special interpolation points, referred to as pivotal points, upon which the interpolation proper will be based. Since the interpolation is anchored to the pivotal points, it is of great importance to the success of the method as a whole that these points be representative of the respective groups and at the same time form a smooth series. Because the interpolating curve segments are constrained either to pass through the pivotal points or, in the modified-interpolation methods, to pass close by them, the entire series will have the same general pattern of regularity as the series of interpolation points.

The simplest method of obtaining the pivotal points is to assume that the ratio of deaths to exposures in each age group is the mortality rate for the central age in the group.

King's method is another method that has been used. King's formulas provide a means of computing the pivotal value, u_x, from three or five of the surrounding quinquennial sums, w_x, into which the data are assumed to be grouped. The formula, based on the three quinquennial sums, w_{x-5}, w_x, and w_{x+5} and correct to third differences, is

$$u_x = .2w_x - .008 \,(w_{x-5} - 2w_x + w_{x+5}).\qquad(3.31)$$

The formula, correct to fifth differences, involves w_{x-10}, w_{x-5}, w_x, w_{x+5} and w_{x+10}. These formulas may be derived by the methods of the theory of finite differences as shown in (10.1). King's formulas should be applied separately to the exposures and deaths. The pivotal values of the rates of mortality are then obtained as the quotient of the pivotal exposures and deaths.

King's method generally will not give satisfactory pivotal points unless the grouped data form a comparatively smooth series as in the case of population statistics where the data are very extensive. In any event, if the series of pivotal points does not seem to be

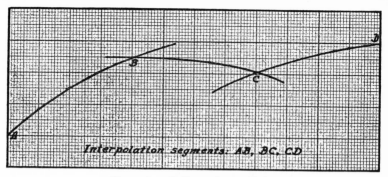

Figure 3a—Ordinary Interpolation

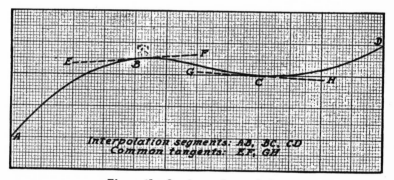

Figure 3b—Osculatory Interpolation

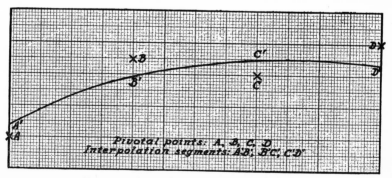

Figure 3c—Modified Osculatory Interpolation

smooth enough, its smoothness may be increased by graduating the pivotal values graphically before proceeding with the interpolation.

3.4 *The interpolation.*

The third step of the interpolation method of graduation is the performance of the interpolation based upon the pivotal points. The intermediate values may be thought of as lying on segments of the interpolating curves determined by the pivotal points, which from now on will be assumed to be numbered consecutively rather than quinquennially.

Historically, the progress of the theory of interpolation has been motivated by the desire to increase the smoothness of the series of interpolated values. A central difference formula, such as Gauss', following, may be used:

$$u_{x+s} = u_x + s\Delta u_x + \frac{s(s-1)}{2!}\Delta^2 u_{x-1} + \frac{s(s^2-1)}{3!}\Delta^3 u_{x-1} + \cdots. \quad (3.41)$$

But, because adjoining curve segments ordinarily do not have equal slopes and derivatives of higher order where they meet, discontinuities are present at the pivotal points which become evident in the interpolated series by a lack of smoothness at these points. (See Figure 3a and note how the interpolating arcs intersect at the pivotal points.)

To remedy this situation, osculatory interpolation was devised by Dr. T. B. Sprague. In the derivation of osculatory interpolation formulas, two adjacent interpolating arcs are required to meet at their common pivotal point in such a way that one or more of the successive derivatives of the interpolating curve functions are equal. The interpolation formulas produced in this way result in interpolated values which differ individually only slightly from those given by ordinary central difference formulas but which collectively form a smooth series from one interval to the next. (See Figure 3b and note how the interpolating arcs join smoothly.)

The simplest formula of this type, based on four pivotal points, is called the Karup-King formula:

$$u_{x+s} = su_{x+1} - \tfrac{1}{2}s^2(1-s)\,\delta^2 u_{x+1} + s'u_x - \tfrac{1}{2}s'^2(1-s')\,\delta^2 u_x, \quad (3.42)$$

where s' means $1-s$. A derivation of the formula is given in (10.2).

Where the pivotal values are not too smooth, a four-point

formula will not give as satisfactory results as a six-point formula, such as Shovelton's:

$$u_{x+s} = su_{x+1} - \tfrac{1}{6}s(1-s^2)\,\delta^2 u_{x+1} + \tfrac{1}{48}s^2(1-s)(5-s)\,\delta^4 u_{x+1}$$
$$+ s'u_x - \tfrac{1}{6}s'(1-s'^2)\,\delta^2 u_x + \tfrac{1}{48}s'^2(1-s')(5-s')\,\delta^4 u_x. \qquad (3.43)$$

The conditions underlying Shovelton's formula are given in (10.3).

The actual computation of the interpolated values is treated in (3.7).

3.5 *Modified osculatory interpolation.*

Both the ordinary interpolation and the osculatory interpolation formulas are true interpolation formulas, in the sense that the interpolating arcs pass through the pivotal points. W. A. Jenkins removed this restriction and produced a set of formulas, known as modified osculatory formulas, which achieve considerably greater smoothness among the interpolated values than do true interpolation formulas.

In the modified osculatory formulas, two adjoining interpolating arcs merely meet and do so in such a way that a specified number of successive derivatives of the interpolating curve functions are equal at their common point. These formulas are illustrated in Figure 3c. Note that the interpolating arcs do not pass through the pivotal points.

The most widely used formula of this type is the fifth difference formula

$$u_{x+s} = s(u_{x+1} - \tfrac{1}{36}\,\delta^4 u_{x+1}) - \tfrac{1}{6}s(1-s^2)(\delta^2 u_{x+1} - \tfrac{1}{6}\,\delta^4 u_{x+1})$$
$$+ s'(u_x - \tfrac{1}{36}\,\delta^4 u_x) - \tfrac{1}{6}s'(1-s'^2)(\delta^2 u_x - \tfrac{1}{6}\,\delta^4 u_x), \qquad (3.51)$$

of which a derivation is given in (10.4). The extent by which values by formula differ from the values at the pivotal points may be ascertained by setting $s = 0$ and $s' = 1$:

$$u_x \text{ (by formula)} = u_x - \tfrac{1}{36}\,\delta^4 u_x.$$

The non-reproduction of the pivotal points allows the interpolation curves to fall among the pivotal values. An element of graduation resulting in greater smoothness is thereby introduced into the interpolation part of the interpolation method. For this reason, the modified osculatory formulas are useful when the series of pivotal points is not quite smooth enough to produce sufficiently smooth interpolated values by other interpolation methods.

3.6 *End values.*

The central formulas quoted do not furnish values in end intervals, so that special treatment of these is necessary. One method is to develop comparable non-symmetrical or advancing-difference formulas which may be applied in those intervals. Another, which almost always produces good results for six-point formulas, is to extend the series assuming the missing fourth differences vanish.

Alternatively, such special devices as the data under consideration suggest may be resorted to. For mortality rates, the table is sometimes extended by using a percentage of the mortality rates of a standard table indicated as being appropriate by the given data; or at the upper end a cubic curve is sometimes fitted to the last three calculated values and the value $q_\omega = 1$ at an arbitrarily determined limiting age.

3.7 *Computation of the interpolated values.*

There are two methods in general use for computing interpolated values. One is to calculate the difference-table and use the formulas in Everett form, e.g., (3.42), (3.43), (3.51). The formula is first written out for the required values of s. Thus (3.43) gives

$$\begin{aligned}
u_{x+.2} &= F_2(x+1) + F_8(x), \\
u_{x+.4} &= F_4(x+1) + F_6(x), \\
u_{x+.6} &= F_6(x+1) + F_4(x), \\
u_{x+.8} &= F_8(x+1) + F_2(x),
\end{aligned} \tag{3.71}$$

where

$$\begin{aligned}
F_2(x) &= .2u_x - .032\,\delta^2 u_x + .0032\,\delta^4 u_x, \\
F_4(x) &= .4u_x - .056\,\delta^2 u_x + .0092\,\delta^4 u_x, \\
F_6(x) &= .6u_x - .064\,\delta^2 u_x + .0132\,\delta^4 u_x, \\
F_8(x) &= .8u_x - .048\,\delta^2 u_x + .0112\,\delta^4 u_x.
\end{aligned} \tag{3.72}$$

If we make the assumption that at the ends the missing fourth differences vanish, we have $\delta^4 u_0 = \delta^4 u_1 = \delta^4 u_{\omega-1} = \delta^4 u_\omega = 0$ and consequently for the missing second differences $\delta^2 u_0 = 2\,\delta^2 u_1 - \delta^2 u_2$, and $\delta^2 u_\omega = 2\,\delta^2 u_{\omega-1} - \delta^2 u_{\omega-2}$. Now by (3.72) we may compute the entire set of $F_2(x)$ from $x=0$ to $x=\omega$, and similarly with $F_4(x)$, $F_6(x)$ and $F_8(x)$. These are added together in pairs (3.71) to produce the interpolated values.

The other method is to work with the interpolation formulas in linear-compound form, in which each interpolated value is expressed in terms of the pivotal u's directly. In the case of (3.43), the expressions are as follows:

$$u_{x+.2} = .0112u_{x-2} - .0896u_{x-1} + .9184u_x + .1904u_{x+1} - .0336u_{x+2}$$
$$+ .0032u_{x+3},$$
$$u_{x+.4} = .0132u_{x-2} - .1076u_{x-1} + .7144u_x + .4504u_{x+1} - .0796u_{x+2}$$
$$+ .0092u_{x+3},$$
$$u_{x+.6} = .0092u_{x-2} - .0796u_{x-1} + .4504u_x + .7144u_{x+1} - .1076u_{x+2}$$
$$+ .0132u_{x+3},$$
$$(3.73)$$
$$u_{x+.8} = .0032u_{x-2} - .0336u_{x-1} + .1904u_x + .9184u_{x+1} - .0896u_{x+2}$$
$$+ .0112u_{x+3}.$$

For the linear-compound method of calculation, the difference-table is needed only at the ends to determine u_{-2}, u_{-1}; $u_{\omega+1}$, $u_{\omega+2}$. The rest of it need not be computed. The elimination of most of the work of deriving the difference table and the relative simplicity of (3.73) tend to make this method the favored one.

3.8 *Exercises.*

3.81 Working with the data of (9.2), obtain pivotal values of q_x for each age group by the use of King's formula (3.31) applied separately to the exposures and deaths. Secure interpolated values of q_x for ages 52 to 67 by one of the quoted formulas.

3.82 Explain and describe the interpolation method of graduation and name a table to which the method was applied.

3.83 What are pivotal values and how are they obtained?

3.84 Discuss the mathematical theory of interpolation in relation to the interpolation method of graduation.

CHAPTER FOUR

The Adjusted-Average Method

4.0 Under the more general heading of graduation by adjusted-average methods are included two sets of graduation formulas—linear-compound formulas and summation formulas. In both types of formulas, each graduated term is determined as a weighted average of a fixed number of ungraduated terms to which it is central. The development of the two sets of formulas, however, arose from widely differing viewpoints.

In the 1870's an American, Erastus L. DeForest, gave a complete treatment of the theory of linear compounding from the standpoint of reduction of error, but since his work was published in obscure journals, it did not become generally known until its discovery by H. H. Wolfenden in 1924. Meanwhile, the English actuaries had developed a number of summation formulas empirically. Summation formulas take their name from the fact that they were constructed in terms of summation operators.

4.1 *Adjusted averages.*

The possibilities of averaging as a graduation device may be readily illustrated numerically. Let the regular series $V_x = 2$, 4, 6, 8, 10, . . . , be assumed to be disturbed by an error series, e_x, introducing irregularities of -1, $+1$, -1, $+1$, . . . , so that the u''_x series actually observed (equal to the sum of the V_x and e_x series) is $u''_x = 1$, 5, 5, 9, 9, ... Averaging the u''_x series in sets of three gives the series $u_x = 3\frac{2}{3}$, $6\frac{1}{3}$, $7\frac{2}{3}$, . . . , corresponding to the 4, 6, 8, . . . , of the original regular series. The u_x series is seen to be a good representation of the underlying regular series with the superimposed error series much reduced.

Both linear-compound and summation formulas are a generalization of this averaging process. The term u_x of the graduated series is expressed as a symmetrical average, or linear compound, of the $2n+1$ ungraduated values, u''_{x+n} to u''_{x-n}, to which it is central:

25

$$u_x = a_n u''_{x+n} + a_{n-1} u''_{x+n-1} + \cdots + a_o u''_x + \cdots + a_{n-1} u''_{x-n+1} + a_n u''_{x-n}.$$

(4.11)

The a_n's are numerical multipliers establishing the proportions in which the respective ungraduated terms enter into the average. In linear-compound formulas, the a_n's are the coefficients of the linear compound, itself, while in summation formulas, they are the coefficients of the linear compound into which the summation operators may be expanded. In both types of formulas, the numerical values of the coefficients are determined so as to secure the formulas likely to be most useful as graduation formulas.

4.2 *The assumptions determining the coefficients.*

The assumptions made for the determination of the values of the coefficients of adjusted-average formulas may best be considered by an analysis of the manner in which such formulas operate.

The ungraduated series is composed of the fundamental underlying series, V_x, and a superimposed error series, e_x, arising from the inherent limitations of observation. The numerical coefficients of an adjusted-average formula useful as a graduation formula must therefore be such that when the formula is applied to an ungraduated series,

(i) the V_x component of the series will be relatively unchanged, and

(ii) the error, e_x, in a particular ungraduated term will be reduced.

The effect of the averaging is to redistribute the error in a particular ungraduated term over the surrounding terms, thereby permitting positive and negative errors partially to offset one another.

Requirement (i) may be stated in another way. If the smooth series, V_x, is considered to be the ungraduated series and is graduated by the application of a linear-compound or summation formula, the terms of the resulting graduated series should not differ materially from the terms of V_x. Since, over a limited range, most regular series met with by the actuary may be closely approximated by a polynomial of the third degree, this condition will ordinarily be met if the graduation formula is made to reproduce such a polynomial without modification. Accordingly, the determination of the values of the coefficients, a_n, is usually made subject to such a requirement.

The determination of numerical multipliers which will allow the reduction of the magnitude of the error component, e_x, may be accomplished in a variety of ways; it is here that the derivation of linear-compound formulas differs from that of summation formulas. In the linear-compound approach, this determination relates to the theory of reduction of error set forth in (4.4) and (4.5), the graduation formula being considered directly in its linear-compound form. In the summation approach described in (4.6), the coefficients are determined through their being expressed in terms of summation operators.

Regardless of how the coefficients of an adjusted-average formula are finally determined, the range of the formula, i.e., the number of terms included in the average, has a material effect on the graduating characteristics of the formula. Within limits, the greater the range of an adjusted-average formula, the greater will be the degree of smoothness possible and the less closely will the graduated series fit the crude data. There are any number of possible adjusted-average formulas of any specified range. The next few articles set forth the means of obtaining formulas with a good combination of fit and smoothness once the range has been decided upon.

Graduation by adjusted-average formulas succeeds as a graduation method because, while the averaging permits the smoothing of the errors in the ungraduated series, the imposition of the condition that a third-degree function be reproduced unchanged generally assures a good representation of the underlying series. Since there are a large number of tested linear-compound and summation formulas available, the application of the method in practice reduces to the choice of a formula appropriate to the particular problem and its use to compute the graduated series.

4.3 *Reproducing a smooth series.*

The conditions which the coefficients of an adjusted-average formula must satisfy in order that when it is applied to a series whose terms are given by a third-degree polynomial the resultant graduated series will be the same series, are obtained by applying (4.11) to the series such that $u''_x = A + Bx + Cx^2 + Dx^3$ for all values of x. Thus,

$$u_x = [a_0 + 2a_1 + 2a_2 + \cdots + 2a_n]A$$
$$+ [a_0 x + a_1(\overline{x-1} + \overline{x+1}) + \cdots + a_n(\overline{x-n} + \overline{x+n})]B$$

$$+[a_0x^2+a_1(\overline{x-1}^2+\overline{x+1}^2)+ \cdots +a_n(\overline{x-n}^2+\overline{x+n}^2)]C$$
$$+[a_0x^3+a_1(\overline{x-1}^3+\overline{x+1}^3)+ \cdots +a_n(\overline{x-n}^3+\overline{x+n}^3)]D$$

$$(4.31)$$

$$=[a_0+2a_1+2a_2+ \cdots +2a_n]A$$
$$+[(a_0+2a_1+ \cdots +2a_n)x]B$$
$$+[(a_0+2a_1+ \cdots +2a_n)x^2+2(a_1+4a_2+ \cdots +n^2a_n)]C$$
$$+[(a_0+2a_1+ \cdots +2a_n)x^3+6(a_1+4a_2+ \cdots +n^2a_n)x]D.$$

Since we want the graduated series to be identical with the ungraduated series, the right hand side of (4.31) must equal $A+Bx+Cx^2+Dx^3$. It follows, therefore, that the conditions are

$$a_0+2a_1+2a_2+ \cdots +2a_n \ =1,$$
$$a_1+2^2a_2+3^2a_3+ \cdots +n^2a_n=0. \qquad (4.32)$$

The assumption made that the underlying fundamental series V_x may be represented by a third-degree polynomial over the range of terms included in the adjusted average is permissible only if the range is not too great. In practice, this limits n to 12 or 13 at most, and the linear compound to not more than 25 or 27 terms. For larger values of n, the formulas produced on this assumption may introduce a material error if, as is generally the case for mortality rates over a substantial range of ages, the V_x underlying series is more nearly a geometric progression than a third-degree polynomial.

4.4 Reduction of mean square error.

The conditions (4.32) just derived are not sufficient to determine all of the linear-compound coefficients, a_n. In the linear-compound approach, the additional conditions which must be imposed follow from considering the effect that the graduation formulas will have on the series of errors, e_x, contained in the ungraduated series.

It is demonstrated in the theory of errors that, if m numerical quantities $z_1, z_2, \ldots, z_m$ are subject, respectively, to the mean square errors $\sigma_1^2, \sigma_2^2, \ldots, \sigma_m^2$, the mean square error in the linear compound, $b_1z_1+b_2z_2+ \cdots +b_mz_m$, is $b_1^2\sigma_1^2+b_2^2\sigma_2^2+ \cdots +b_m^2\sigma_m^2$. This is demonstrated on pp. 23-25 of "The Fundamental Principles of Mathematical Statistics" by H. H. Wolfenden, to which the student may refer. If all of the σ^2's may be considered equal ($=\sigma^2$), the mean square error of the linear compound is thus

$$(b_1^2+b_2^2+ \cdots +b_m^2)\sigma^2. \qquad (4.41)$$

If, then, we make the not unreasonable assumption that the mean square errors of the u_x'''s are substantially the same ($=e^2$), the mean square error in each graduated value will be

$$(a_0{}^2+2a_1{}^2+2a_2{}^2+\cdots+2a_n{}^2)e^2.$$

The mean square error in the graduated value will thus, on the average, be reduced by the application of the graduation formula so that the proportion it will bear to the mean square error of the ungraduated value is

$$(a_0{}^2+2a_1{}^2+2a_2{}^2+\cdots+2a_n{}^2):1. \qquad (4.42)$$

This ratio is usually denoted by $R_0{}^2$, and, as we have seen, it represents the reduction in mean square error attributable to graduation. The reciprocal of $R_0{}^2$ is sometimes called the Weight, W, of a graduation formula. The appropriateness of this term arises from the fact that the same degree of reduction in mean square error could theoretically be accomplished by dealing with a larger experience in which each exposure was multiplied by W.

For a given value of n, the a_n's can be determined to produce a maximum reduction of mean square error by the methods of the differential calculus applied to minimize (4.42), subject, of course, to the conditions (4.32), which are applicable in any event. The derivation is given in (10.5). The numerical values of the coefficients of the 17-term formula of maximum Weight are shown in (4.7).

Formulas of maximum Weight are sometimes used for special purposes, such as the determination of pivotal values for a graduation by interpolation. However, for general use they prove to be somewhat disappointing in that they tend to over-graduate; that is, to eliminate as irregularities what are actually significant features of the data. For this reason, the emphasis on reduction of error was gradually transferred to the reduction of the mean square errors in various orders of differences rather than in the graduated values themselves. The resulting formulas have been found to give both greater smoothness and a closer fit than formulas of maximum Weight.

4.5 *Reduction of mean square error in the differences.*

The extent of the reduction of the mean square error in the third differences may be readily computed. If the observed values are subject to a mean square error of e^2, their third differences,

$u''_{x+3} - 3u''_{x+2} + 3u''_{x+1} - u''_x$, will be subject to one of $(1^2 + 3^2 + 3^2 + 1^2)e^2$, or $20e^2$.

The mean square error in the third differences of the graduated values may be computed by writing out $u_{x+3} - 3u_{x+2} + 3u_{x+1} - u_x$ in terms of the u''_x's and the linear compound coefficients, a_n, and applying the basic relation (4.41). The result is $\left[\sum_{-n-3}^{n} (\Delta^3 a_i)^2 \right] \cdot e^2$,

where the third differences of the a_n's are obtained by differencing the complete set of a_n's (from $-n$ to $+n$, including as zeros any coefficients that are equal to zero) augmented by three zero values at each end. (Note that there are three more $\Delta^3 a_n$'s than originally there were a_n's.)

The reduction of mean square error of the third differences is thus, on the average, in the ratio of

$$\frac{1}{20}\left[\sum_{-n-3}^{n} (\Delta^3 a_i)^2 \right] : 1, \qquad (4.51)$$

which is usually written R_3^2. The value of R_3 is sometimes referred to as the smoothing coefficient of the graduation formula and used as a measure of the smoothing power of the formula.

The formulas producing the maximum reduction of mean square error in the third differences are derived by a straightforward application of the differential calculus minimizing (4.51), subject to the conditions (4.32). (Refer to (10.6).) The coefficients of the 17-term formula which effects the maximum reduction in third-difference error are given in (4.7).

4.6 *Summation formulas.*

Linear-compound formulas such as the minimum R_0 and R_3 formulas are easy to use if the multiplications can be done on a calculating machine. The summation formulas of the English actuaries were developed before the general introduction of these machines. They were constructed in terms of summation operators, involving easily performed arithmetical operations.

The summation operator $[p]$ applied to the series u''_x means the calculation of a new value u_x by summing the p terms of the u''_x series centering about u''_x; $\dfrac{[p]}{p} u''_x$ means the average of the p terms of the u''_x series. Thus

$$\frac{[p]}{p}u''_x = \frac{1}{p}\left\{ u''_{x+\frac{p-1}{2}} + u''_{x+\frac{p-3}{2}} + \cdots + u''_{x-\frac{p-1}{2}} \right\}.$$

The illustration of averaging given in (4.1) is an instance of the application of the operator $\dfrac{[3]}{3}$. It is obvious that this single averaging process tends to reduce the error component of an ungraduated series. However, the operator expanded in terms of differences is

$$\frac{[p]}{p} = 1 + \frac{(p^2-1)}{24}\delta^2 + \frac{(p^2-1)(p^2-9)}{1920}\delta^4 + \cdots, \qquad (4.61)$$

from which it can be seen that its application to a third-degree function will not reproduce it unchanged. An error equal in amount to $\dfrac{(p^2-1)}{24}$ times the second difference of the function is introduced. The use of three successive averages,

$$\frac{[p]\,[q]\,[r]}{pqr}, \qquad (4.62)$$

produces an even more pronounced leveling effect on the series of errors than the use of only one, but the error resulting from its application to a third-degree function is thereby increased to $\dfrac{(p^2+q^2+r^2-3)}{24}\delta^2$.

This defect may be counteracted by a simple device. Instead of applying (4.62) to a series of ungraduated values directly, the series is first adjusted in such a manner as to counteract the systematic errors that (4.62) would otherwise introduce. This is accomplished by taking a simple linear compound of the ungraduated series (extending over not more than seven terms) designed so as to counteract the error in $\dfrac{[p]\,[q]\,[r]}{pqr}$ and render the combination correct to third differences. For example, the operation, $\dfrac{[5]\,[5]\,[5]}{125}$, introduces a systematic error of $\dfrac{(5^2+5^2+5^2-3)}{24}\delta^2 = 3\,\delta^2$ in a third-degree polynomial. If each of the terms, u''_x, is first replaced by

$$-u''_{x-2} + u''_{x-1} + u''_x + u''_{x+1} - u''_{x+2},$$

it may be shown by expressing the adjustment in terms of differences that an error of $-3\delta^2$ is thereby introduced in each term. The combination of these two operations produces Higham's formula:

$$u_x = \frac{[5]^3}{125}(-u''_{x-2}+u''_{x-1}+u''_x+u''_{x+1}-u''_{x+2}), \qquad (4.63)$$

which will reproduce a third-degree polynomial exactly. If this formula is expressed in linear-compound form, it will be found to involve 17 ungraduated terms (two with zero coefficients). The coefficients appear in (4.7).

In this fashion, a number of summation formulas were created. Most of them involve three averaging operations applied to a series which has been adjusted to counteract their systematic second-difference error. It will be noted that, while all summation formulas may be expressed in linear-compound form, the reverse is not true, because of the limitation implicitly imposed on the values of the numerical coefficients in order for them to be expressible in summation form. With the calculating machines in use today, it is usually more satisfactory to use the linear-compound formulas developed to achieve reduction of error since they tend to produce somewhat better graduations than comparable summation formulas.

4.7 *Coefficients of 17-term formulas.*

The coefficients of the 17-term formulas of maximum Weight and of minimum smoothing coefficient and of Higham's formula are shown together in the following table in order to facilitate their comparison.

n	Minimum R_0 Formula (Maximum Weight)	Minimum R_3 Formula (Minimum Smoothing Coefficient)	Higham's Summation Formula
0	.1330	.1892	.2000
±1	.1301	.1764	.1920
±2	.1208	.1411	.1440
±3	.1052	.0923	.0800
±4	.0836	.0421	.0240
±5	.0557	.0025	.0000
±6	.0217	−.0186	−.0160
±7	−.0186	−.0204	−.0160
±8	−.0650	−.0100	−.0080

Note that the sum of the coefficients of each of the formulas is one. It will be found that the second of equations (4.32) is also satisfied.

4.8 *End values.*

Because the end terms are not reached by the symmetrical formulas, adjusted-average methods require the use of special devices if the table is to be completed for all ages for which there were ungraduated values. The nature of these devices depends on practical considerations, on the form and extent of the data and the function being graduated.

In working with rates of mortality, the graduated table may be completed by merging it with a percentage, derived from the experience being graduated, of the mortality rates of some standard table indicated as being suitable. At the older ages, a cubic curve is sometimes fitted to the last three graduated values and the value $q_\omega = 1$ at an arbitrarily determined limiting age; or the graduated series is sometimes extended by assuming it to be a geometrical progression with common ratio of about 1.1.

4.9 *Exercises.*

4.91 Graduate the ratios of actual to expected in (9.3) by the minimum R_3 formula and by Higham's formula (4.63). Compare the graduated and ungraduated series graphically. For one of these formulas, calculate the graduated rates of mortality and the graduated deaths and apply tests of smoothness and fit to them.

4.92 Give an explanation of the principles underlying the method of graduation by summation or linear-compound formulas.

4.93 How are the values of the coefficients of linear-compound formulas determined? Those of summation formulas?

4.94 Define reduction of error and explain its application to linear-compound formulas.

CHAPTER FIVE

The Difference-Equation Method

5.0 Professor E. T. Whittaker of the University of Edinburgh first enunciated the principles of the difference-equation method in a paper published in 1919. Subsequently, Robert Henderson developed a practical process for employing the method to make a numerical graduation. For these reasons, difference-equation formulas are also referred to as Whittaker-Henderson formulas.

5.1 *The basis of the method.*

The method is founded on the formulation of an analytic expression measuring the combination of smoothness and fit. These concepts were discussed in a general way in (1.3). Methods of measuring smoothness were defined in (1.7). Closeness of fit was expressed in (1.8) in terms of $\Sigma E_x(q_x - q''_x)$. For the sake of simplicity, we will for the present assume that

(i) Smoothness is adequately measured by the smallness of the sum of the squares of the second differences of the graduated values:

$$S = \Sigma(\Delta^2 q_x)^2 = \Sigma(q_{x+2} - 2q_{x+1} + q_x)^2; \qquad (5.11)$$

(ii) Closeness of fit is adequately measured by the smallness of

$$F = \Sigma(q_x - q''_x)^2. \qquad (5.12)$$

The combination of smoothness and fit may then be expressed as and measured by

$$F + hS, \qquad (5.13)$$

where h is a positive number fixing the relative weight assigned to smoothness and fit. The smaller $F + hS$ for a given value of h, the better the graduation will be.

Different values of h will produce different graduations. The value selected controls the relationship between smoothness and fit. If h is small, the graduated values will be fairly close to the

34

ungraduated values; as h is increased, the divergence will increase until smoothness is favored over fit. At one end of the scale, $h=0$ corresponds to no graduation at all for the graduated series will be identical with the ungraduated series; at the other end of the scale, $h=\infty$ results in a straight line of graduated values—the one which would be fitted to the q_x'''s by the method of least squares.

5.2 *Derivation of the difference equation.*

The best graduation, according to our assumptions, will result from requiring $F+hS$ to be as small as possible.

The derivation of the difference equation is based on the fact that each of the $\omega+1$ graduated q_x's can be considered as an independent variable and $F+hS$ as a function of these independent variables, the values of the ungraduated q_x'''s being a set of given constants.

The necessary conditions for a minimum come from the differential calculus. They consist of the equations resulting from setting equal to zero each partial derivative of $F+hS$ with respect to an independent variable.

Let q_x be one particular q. Since the q's are independent variables, if q_y is one of the other q's,

$$\frac{\partial q_y}{\partial q_x}=0,$$

and there is only one term in F involving q_x. Thus

$$\frac{\partial F}{\partial q_x}=\frac{\partial(q_x-q_x'')^2}{\partial q_x}=2(q_x-q_x'').$$

There are three terms in S involving q_x, and we find

$$\frac{\partial S}{\partial q_x}=\frac{\partial}{\partial q_x}[(q_{x+2}-2q_{x+1}+q_x)^2+(q_{x+1}-2q_x+q_{x-1})^2\\+(q_x-2q_{x-1}+q_{x-2})^2]$$
$$=2(q_{x+2}-2q_{x+1}+q_x)-4(q_{x+1}-2q_x+q_{x-1})+2(q_x-2q_{x-1}+q_{x-2})$$
$$=2(q_{x+2}-4q_{x+1}+6q_x-4q_{x-1}+q_{x-2})=2\,\delta^4 q_x.$$

The conditions for a minimum are thus of the form

$$(q_x-q_x'')+h\,\delta^4 q_x=0,$$

or

$$q_x''=q_x+h\,\delta^4 q_x. \tag{5.21}$$

This relationship is called a linear difference equation of the fourth order. Graduation formulas based upon (5.21) are among those known as Whittaker-Henderson Type A graduation formulas.

Before going on to describe the practical solution, it is well to recapitulate briefly the steps by which we arrived at (5.21):

(i) Setting up formulas for measuring smoothness and fit;

(ii) Establishing the combination of the two in terms of the constant h, which controls the balance between smoothness and fit;

(iii) Deriving the difference equation by the use of the differential calculus.

5.3 *The practical method of solving the difference equation.*

Formula A is used to graduate a great many other series than rates of mortality. For this reason, (5.21) is usually written in terms of u_x's rather than q_x's. The plain u_x's refer to the graduated series, the u_x'''s to the ungraduated series. In terms of these u_x's equation (5.21) becomes

$$u_x'' = u_x + h \, \delta^4 u_x. \qquad (5.31)$$

The Henderson process for solving (5.31) is based on the fact that the equation may be factored in terms of its finite-difference operators and, by the introduction of the intermediate series, u_x', be replaced by two simpler difference equations:

$$u_x'' = \tfrac{1}{2}(a+1)(a+2)u_x' - a(a+2)u_{x-1}' + \tfrac{1}{2}a(a+1)u_{x-2}', \quad (5.32a)$$
$$u_x' = \tfrac{1}{2}(a+1)(a+2)u_x - a(a+2)u_{x+1} + \tfrac{1}{2}a(a+1)u_{x+2}; \quad (5.32b)$$

provided h and a are connected by the relationship

$$h = \tfrac{1}{4}a(a+1)^2(a+2). \qquad (5.33)$$

The actual factorization of (5.31) is demonstrated in (10.7).

That the two equations (5.32a) and (5.32b) are equivalent to (5.31) may be verified by substituting the u_x''s obtained from (5.32b) in (5.32a).

These two second-order difference equations are used in the form

$$u_x' = \frac{2a}{a+1}u_{x-1}' - \frac{a}{a+2}u_{x-2}' + \frac{2}{(a+1)(a+2)}u_x'', \qquad (5.34a)$$
$$u_x = \frac{2a}{a+1}u_{x+1} - \frac{a}{a+2}u_{x+2} + \frac{2}{(a+1)(a+2)}u_x'. \qquad (5.34b)$$

If two u_x''s at the zero end are supposed to be known, all the subsequent u'_x's may be found, in order, by (5.34a). If two u_x's at the other end can be found, the rest of the graduated series may be derived, in reverse order, by (5.34b). The only further problem that must be solved is the determination of these four "starting values."

It may be shown (see (10.8)) that the two u_x's at the ω-end can always be found accurately as soon as the intermediate u'_x series has been calculated. They are

$$u_{\omega-1} = u'_{\omega-1} + a\Delta u'_{\omega-1},$$
$$u_\omega = u'_\omega + a\Delta u'_{\omega-1}. \tag{5.35}$$

At the zero end of the series, the two needed values of u'_x cannot be determined accurately at the outset except by involved methods. If such methods are not to be resorted to, the first two graduated values must be estimated from the general run of the ungraduated values at the zero end. The graduation is completed using these estimated values and then corrected, if necessary. This procedure may be summarized as follows:

(i) On a graph of the first 4 or 5 u''_x's, a straight line is drawn as an approximation to the graduated values, and $u*_0$ and $u*_1$ (estimated values of u_0 and u_1) are read from the graph.

(ii) The starting values are computed from

$$u'_{-2} = u*_0 - (a+2)\Delta u*_0,$$
$$u'_{-1} = u*_1 - (a+2)\Delta u*_0. \tag{5.36}$$

These equations are analogous to (5.35) and are based on the theoretical relationship between the u'_x series and the graduated series at the zero end. (See (10.8).)

(iii) If the estimated values, $u*_0$ and $u*_1$, were good estimates, then the resultant graduated values u_0 and u_1 should be substantially in agreement with them. If, after performing the graduation, this is found not to be the case, corrected values of u_0 and u_1 may be calculated by the formulas:

(corrected u_0)
$$= u_0 + \frac{a(2a+5)}{a+2}(u_0 - u*_0) - \frac{2a(a+1)}{a+2}(u_1 - u*_1),$$
(5.37)

(corrected u_1)
$$= u_1 + \frac{2a(a^2+2a-1)}{(a+1)(a+2)}(u_0 - u*_0) - \frac{a(2a-1)}{a+2}(u_1 - u*_1).$$

Revised starting values may then be computed by (5.36) and the entire graduation reworked to secure the remainder of the corrected graduated series. The derivation of equations (5.37) is given in (10.9).

5.4 *Numerical example.*

It is almost essential to work through a numerical example of a graduation by Formula A in order to gain an understanding of the method. We will graduate a series for the case $a = 2$.

When $a = 2$, $h = 18$, and the graduating equations are

$$u'_x = \tfrac{4}{3}u'_{x-1} - \tfrac{1}{2}u'_{x-2} + \tfrac{1}{6}u''_x, \qquad (5.41a)$$
$$u_x = \tfrac{4}{3}u_{x+1} - \tfrac{1}{2}u_{x+2} + \tfrac{1}{6}u'_x. \qquad (5.41b)$$

The first step is to estimate the first two graduated u_x's. In the example shown in the following table, a rough graph gives $u^*_0 = 26$, $u^*_1 = 29$. By (5.36), $u'_{-2} = 14$ and $u'_{-1} = 17$. Entering these values in column (3) below, we fill in the rest of the column by (5.41a). Thus

$$u'_0 = \tfrac{4}{3}(17) - \tfrac{1}{2}(14) + \tfrac{1}{6}(34) = 21.33,$$
$$u'_1 = \tfrac{4}{3}(21.33) - \tfrac{1}{2}(17) + \tfrac{1}{6}(24) = 23.94, \text{ etc.}$$

The work is carried along until the computation of $u'_{18} = 107.96$. Then, by (5.35), we compute $u_{17} = 117.34$ and $u_{18} = 126.72$. Next, the rest of column (4) is filled in from the bottom up by the use of (5.41b). Thus

$$u_{16} = \tfrac{4}{3}(117.34) - \tfrac{1}{2}(126.72) + \tfrac{1}{6}(91.61) = 108.36, \text{ etc.}$$

The graduation looks pretty good, in that the calculated values u_0 and u_1 are in good agreement with u^*_0 and u^*_1. If it is considered advisable to perfect the graduation, (5.37) gives the true values of u_0 and u_1 as

$$(\text{corrected } u_0) = 26.38 + \tfrac{9}{2}\,(26.38 - 26) - 3(29.25 - 29) = 27.34,$$
$$(\text{corrected } u_1) = 29.25 + \tfrac{7}{3}\,(26.38 - 26) - \tfrac{3}{2}\,(29.25 - 29) = 29.76.$$

By (5.36), these give $u'_{-2} = 17.66$ and $u'_{-1} = 20.08$, as the new starting values, which may be used to compute the corrected graduated series. Ordinarily it would not be worth while to make such small corrections.

The steps in making a graduation by Formula A may be summarized as follows:

(i) Choosing a value for the constant a (or h) which is appropriate to the data;

(ii) Obtaining u^*_0 and u^*_1, the approximate values of the first two u_x's by graphic or other means;

(iii) Calculating u'_{-2} and u'_{-1}, the starting u'_x's, by (5.36);

(iv) Calculating the u'_x column by (5.34a);

(v) Calculating $u_{\omega-1}$ and u_ω by (5.35);

(vi) Calculating the balance of the u_x column by (5.34b);

(vii) Optional correction by (5.37).

Specimen Graduation by Formula A

(1)	(2)	(3)	(4)
x	u''_x	u'_x	u_x
−2	——	(14.00)	——
−1	——	(17.00)	——
0	34	21.33	26.38
1	24	23.94	29.25
2	31	26.42	32.35
3	40	29.93	35.74
4	30	31.70	39.40
5	49	35.47	43.56
6	48	39.44	47.92
7	48	42.86	52.49
8	67	48.60	57.27
9	58	53.04	62.02
10	67	57.59	67.03
11	75	62.77	72.44
12	76	67.56	78.32
13	76	71.36	84.91
14	102	78.37	92.29
15	100	85.48	100.06
16	101	91.61	108.36
17	115	98.58	(117.34)
18	134	107.96	(126.72)
	1,275		1,273.85

5.5 Other Type A formulas.

The difference-equation method is not limited to graduation formulas based on equation (5.21). Other difference equations involving differences of other orders may be derived by modifying the measure of smoothness (5.11). There is a family of Type A formulas corresponding to each such difference equation.

For instance, if $\Sigma(\Delta^3 q_x)^2$ is used instead of $\Sigma(\Delta^2 q_x)^2$ as the measure of smoothness, the difference equation resulting from the minimization of $\Sigma(q_x - q''_x)^2 + k\Sigma(\Delta^3 q_x)^2$ and corresponding to (5.21) is of the sixth order:

$$q''_x = q_x - k\,\delta^6 q_x, \tag{5.51}$$

where k is a positive number. The graduation is accomplished in the same way as for the fourth-order difference equation, by a factorization of (5.51) similar to that appearing in (5.3) and the use of an intermediate series defined analogously to (5.34a) and (5.34b). However, three starting values are required at each end.

5.6 Type B formulas.

A set of difference-equation formulas known as Whittaker-Henderson Type B formulas may be developed by modifying the measure of fit (5.12) so as to take into account the value of the exposures at each age. The measure of fit may be taken as the smallness of $\Sigma E_x(q_x - q''_x)^2$. This may be combined with a measure of smoothness based on any desired order of differences.

For the third-difference criterion of smoothness, the function to be minimized is

$$\Sigma E_x(q''_x - q_x)^2 + k\Sigma(\Delta^3 q_x)^2, \tag{5.61}$$

and the resulting difference equation is

$$E_x q''_x = E_x q_x - k\,\delta^6 q_x. \tag{5.62}$$

The method of solution involves the solution of $\omega + 1$ equations in $\omega + 1$ unknowns. The graduation, which automatically weights the observations at each age in proportion to the exposures, is usually excellent, but the working process is long and difficult. For this reason, Formula B is rarely used except for making graduations of considerable importance.

5.7 Exercises.

5.71 Apply the Whittaker-Henderson Type A formula (fourth-order difference equation) with $a = 1$ to the ratios of actual to expected mortality in (9.3). Calculate the graduated rates of mortality and the graduated deaths and apply tests of smoothness and fit to them. Compare the results of this graduation with the graduation by the adjusted-average method (4.91).

5.72 State the principles upon which Whittaker-Henderson graduation formulas are based.

5.73 How is the difference equation derived in the difference-equation method? What are "starting values"?

5.74 Without giving specific formulas, outline Henderson's process for calculating the numerical values of a graduated series by the application of a fourth-order Type A difference equation.

5.75 What is the difference in theory underlying the Whittaker-Henderson Type A formulas and Type B formulas?

CHAPTER SIX

Graduation by Mathematical Formula

6.0 Graduation by mathematical formula, or curve fitting, as distinguished from the other methods of graduation, was developed primarily outside of the field of actuarial mathematics. There is a large variety of curves which may be used in representing different types of statistical data. They range from the simple straight line to the family of frequency curves developed by Karl Pearson and to the curve systems of Gram-Charlier, Poisson and Fourier. There is voluminous literature on the applicability of various types of curves and on the methods of fitting them.

The curves of commonest use and maximum interest to the actuary in treating mortality rates are Gompertz' and Makeham's curves, which were developed in the search for a mathematical law of mortality. Their use has the distinct advantage of permitting the application of the principle of uniform seniority, which so greatly simplifies the calculation of joint life functions—annuity values, premiums and reserves.

6.1 *Graduation by mathematical formula.*

In the method of graduation by mathematical formula, the graduated series is represented by a mathematical curve fitted to the data. The application of the method involves two steps:

(i) The choice of the form of curve to represent the graduated series;

(ii) The determination of the constants of the curve.

Mathematical curves chosen for this purpose are smooth, continuous, differentiable and usually involve relatively few parameters, or constants. The parabola, the normal probability curve and the Gompertz curve are examples of such curves. While tests applicable to the data are sometimes helpful, the selection of an appropriate type of curve is largely a matter of experience.

The curve fitting, i.e., the determination of the constants of the curve, is usually done by the method of moments or least squares, or by some modification of them. It is customary to require that the graduated and ungraduated values agree in their totals and in at least their first moments.

6.11 *The graduation of exposures and deaths.*

Graduated mortality rates are sometimes secured by graduating exposures and deaths separately. They are not graduated independently, however, because such a procedure would fail to take cognizance of the connection existing in the data between the exposed to risk and deaths at the same age.

First a curve is fitted to the exposures. The body of exposed to risk constitutes a frequency distribution, and the appropriate curve is usually one of the standard frequency curves. After this has been done, the observed mortality rates are multiplied by the corresponding graduated exposures and a second frequency curve is fitted to these recomputed deaths, or they are graduated by some other method. Then the graduated mortality rates are calculated by dividing the graduated deaths by the graduated exposed to risk.

This procedure takes account directly of the weight of the observations at individual ages, for it is, in effect, the graduation of the observed mortality rates weighted at each age by the corresponding exposures. While the weights actually employed are the graduated exposed to risk, they are approximately the same as, and for purposes of weighting, are equivalent to the actual exposures.

6.2 *Gompertz' and Makeham's formulas.*

Gompertz' and Makeham's formulas have been employed frequently to represent insured and annuitant mortality. This they have been able to do fairly successfully over a relatively wide range of ages—from about age twenty to the limit of the table.

The formulas are expressible in several different ways: in terms of the number living, l_x; the force of mortality, μ_x; and the cologarithm of the probability of living, colog p_x.

Gompertz' Formula	*Makeham's Formula*	
$l_x = kg^{c^x},$	$l_x = ks^x g^{c^x},$	(6.21)
$\mu_x = Bc^x,$	$\mu_x = A + Bc^x,$	(6.22)
colog $p_x = \beta c^x,$	colog $p_x = a + \beta c^x.$	(6.23)

The form is the same for μ_x and colog p_x; in fact, A equals a. However, since μ_x and colog p_x are not equal, the values of the constants B and β differ.

A simple test, applied to the observed data, will determine whether a Gompertz or Makeham fit should be attempted. From Gompertz' formula, we have

$$\operatorname{colog}_5 p_{x+5}/\operatorname{colog}_5 p_x = c^5, \qquad (6.24)$$

where $\operatorname{colog}_5 p_x = \operatorname{colog} p_x + \operatorname{colog} p_{x+1} + \cdots + \operatorname{colog} p_{x+4}$.

If the ratios (6.24) computed from the data are nearly constant, a Gompertz fit is suggested. For Makeham's formula, denoting differences over a five-year interval by Δ,

$$\Delta \operatorname{colog}_5 p_{x+5}/\Delta \operatorname{colog}_5 p_x = c^5, \qquad (6.25)$$

and if the ratios (6.25) calculated from the data are almost constant, a satisfactory Makeham fit may be possible.

Since Makeham's formula includes Gompertz' as a limiting form, when A equals a equals zero, the succeeding articles of this chapter will not always refer specifically to the latter.

6.3 *The Makeham constants.*

In discussing methods of securing the numerical values of the Makeham constants, two situations are to be distinguished. In the first, a Makeham curve is to be fitted to data already smooth, presumably having been graduated by some other means. In the second, the Makeham formula is to be based directly upon the observed data.

In the first case, a satisfactory fit may often be secured by choosing four equidistant widely-spaced values of l_x and solving the set of simultaneous equations resulting from the substitution of these values in the formula. From (6.21), taking logarithms, we have the following equations from which the four constants may be derived:

$$\begin{aligned}
\log l_x &= \log k + x \log s + c^x \log g, \\
\log l_{x+t} &= \log k + (x+t) \log s + c^{x+t} \log g, \\
\log l_{x+2t} &= \log k + (x+2t) \log s + c^{x+2t} \log g, \\
\log l_{x+3t} &= \log k + (x+3t) \log s + c^{x+3t} \log g.
\end{aligned} \qquad (6.31)$$

For Gompertz' formula, three values of l_x and three such equations would suffice.

In the second situation, it is not advisable to determine the numerical values of the constants by the use of isolated points for, on account of the irregularity of the observed series, different sets of points would produce widely varying values. There is no way of choosing four points beforehand with any assurance of obtaining a suitable representation of the data. For this reason, when the graduation is to be based directly on the observed data, other methods of determining the constants are customarily employed. They involve the use of all or a large part of the data and consequently are more faithful in bringing out the general characteristics of the underlying series.

6.4 *Hardy's method of calculating the value of c.*

The first step is to determine the value of the constant c, which, as it happens, is such that $\log_{10} c$ usually lies between .035 and .045. G. F. Hardy suggests the use of 12 quinquennial values of $\mu_{x+\frac{1}{2}}$ calculated from the data by applying King's formula (3.31) to the exposures and deaths grouped into five year age groups and then making use of the approximation $\mu_{x+\frac{1}{2}} = \dfrac{\Theta_x}{E_x - \frac{1}{2}\Theta_x}$. The μ's should lie in the part of the experience where the exposure is heaviest. For its additional graduating effect, weighting is used with the weights 1, 3, 5, 5, 3, 1.

Applying the weights to the first six values of $\mu_{x+\frac{1}{2}}$ and summing, we have

$$\Sigma_1 = 18A + Bc^{x+\frac{1}{2}}(1 + 3c^5 + 5c^{10} + 5c^{15} + 3c^{20} + c^{25}).$$

In a similar manner, using the middle six values of $\mu_{x+\frac{1}{2}}$,

$$\Sigma_2 = 18A + Bc^{x+15\frac{1}{2}}f(c),$$

and from the last six values of $\mu_{x+\frac{1}{2}}$,

$$\Sigma_3 = 18A + Bc^{x+30\frac{1}{2}}f(c).$$

Then,

$$\frac{\Sigma_3 - \Sigma_2}{\Sigma_2 - \Sigma_1} = \frac{Bc^{x+15\frac{1}{2}}(c^{15} - 1)f(c)}{Bc^{x+\frac{1}{2}}(c^{15} - 1)f(c)} = c^{15} \tag{6.41}$$

from which c may be calculated.

6.5 *The values of A and B.*

With the value of c known, A and B can be found from the two equations which express the reproduction by the graduated values of the sum of the actual deaths and the average age at death. We have, approximately,

$$\frac{\Theta_x}{L_x} = \mu_{x+\frac{1}{2}} = A + Bc^{x+\frac{1}{2}}. \tag{6.51}$$

In order to make the total deaths and the average age at death equal for the graduated and ungraduated values, we must solve the following pair of simultaneous equations for A and B:

$$\Sigma\Theta_x = A\Sigma L_x + B\Sigma L_x c^{x+\frac{1}{2}} = \Sigma\Theta''_x, \tag{6.52a}$$

$$\Sigma x\Theta_x = A\Sigma x L_x + B\Sigma x L_x c^{x+\frac{1}{2}} = \Sigma x\Theta''_x, \tag{6.52b}$$

where L_x may be computed from the approximation

$$L_x = E_x - \frac{1}{2}\Theta''_x.$$

6.6 *Graphical method for the Makeham constants.*

There is a graphical method for approximately determining the Makeham constants which has the advantage that, in the course of its application, it shows whether the data lie near enough to a Makeham curve to make the fitting of such a curve worthwhile. If a Makeham fit proves to be feasible and it is felt desirable to have more refined values for the constants, they may be redetermined by the methods of (6.4) and (6.5). Sometimes, the value of c determined graphically is retained and the redetermination limited to the values of A and B.

The method is based on the fact that if an expression of the form Bc^x is plotted on semi-logarithmic paper, such as is described in (2.4) and pictured in Figure 4 illustrating the method, the result is a straight line. If μ_x follows the law $\mu_x = A + Bc^x$, it must thus be possible to find a value of A for which such a graph of $\mu_x - A$ is a straight line.

The first step is to compute values of μ_x at quinquennial intervals, which may be done by the process described in the first paragraph of (6.4). These are then plotted on semi-logarithmic paper. Next, the values of $\mu_x - .001$ are plotted. If a curve is drawn roughly through the first set of points, it will be found to be concave up. The curve through the second set may also be concave up. This means that the constant A is greater than .001. If it is concave down, $A < .001$.

For other values of A, plot sets of points corresponding to

$\mu_x - A_1$, $\mu_x - A_2$, ..., until the set is found that most nearly lies on a straight line. It is well to write the relative exposures on the graph as this goal is approached so that the graduator may be able to see at a glance which points are the most important.

Having decided upon the value of A which gives the best set of points, the graduator draws the corresponding straight line. From this line, c may be found by taking any point $\mu_{x_1} - A$ and locating the age x_2 corresponding to the ordinate $10(\mu_{x_1} - A)$. When the ages x_1 and x_2 have been selected in this way,

$$\log (\mu_{x_2} - A) = \log 10 \ (\mu_{x_1} - A). \tag{6.61}$$

Thence, $\log B + x_2 \log c = \log 10 + \log B + x_1 \log c$ \hfill (6.62)

and $$\log_{10} c = \frac{1}{x_2 - x_1}. \tag{6.63}$$

The value of $\log B$ may now be found from any point on the line:

$$\log B = \log (\mu_x - A) - x \log c \tag{6.64}$$

6.7 *Adjustments at the young adult ages.*

Mortality rates at the young adult ages, from about age 20 to 35, are often rather flat. Sometimes they may exhibit a slight rise followed by a decline, which appears as a hump in the curve of mortality.

The Gompertz and Makeham curves have no maxima or minima or points of inflexion and so are not adaptable without modification to peculiarities such as may be present at the young adult ages. It has been possible, however, to maintain their usefulness over a wide range of ages by suitable modification of the constants.

A variation by age in the constant A or a is sometimes introduced. For example, in the graduation of the Combined Annuity Table, we find

$$\text{colog } p_x = 10^{.035(x-117)} + \begin{cases} .000487 \dotfill \text{under 21} \\ .000487 \ \dfrac{(35-x)^2(2x-25)}{3375} \dotfill 21\text{-}35 \\ 0 \dotfill 35 \text{ and over.} \end{cases}$$

For Ages

6.8 *Exercises.*

6.81 Fit Makeham's formula to the data of (9.2). Secure a value for c by Hardy's method, (6.4). Then calculate A and B by equa-

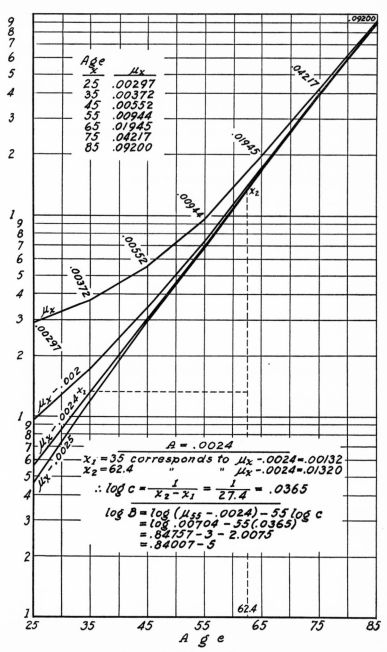

Figure 4—Makeham Constants

tions (6.52). Also, determine the values of the Makeham constants by the graphic method described in (6.6).

6.82 What is the basis of the method of graduation by mathematical formulas? What steps are involved?

6.83 What tests would you make to determine whether to attempt a graduation by Gompertz' or Makeham's formula? What adjustment would normally be required at the lower ages?

6.84 How would you go about performing a graduation by Makeham's formula?

6.85 How are exposures and deaths graduated separately by mathematical formula? What is the advantage of doing so?

CHAPTER SEVEN

Select Tables

7.0 The first six chapters have been confined to a consideration of graduation as a problem in terms of a single variable; the problem of graduation also arises in connection with functions of more than one variable. The first investigations into actuarial functions of this sort were made about 1875 by Sprague and King. These were studies of the rate of mortality of insured lives by duration from issue age as well as by attained age.

Tables constructed to show rates of mortality by age and duration are referred to as select tables. The use of the term "select" arose from the fact that the variation by duration may be considered to be the result of medical, or other selection at issue. Duration is also often a second variable in connection with such other actuarial functions as disability rates, rates of termination among disabled lives, lapse rates and rates of termination of employment.

Actuarial functions are not restricted to the variables age and duration, nor are they limited to a maximum of two variables. For example, the variation in mortality rates by calendar year has also been considered.

7.1 *Select tables.*

The graduation of functions of more than one variable is identical in principle with that of functions of one variable. The problem arises in the same way and the justifications for the process of graduation are the same. The problem may be stated as that of securing from an irregular, observed multiple series of data a smooth, regular "surface" of values consistent with the array of observed values. Instead of a mortality curve, we have to deal with a mortality surface.

The graphic method, the interpolation method, the adjusted-average method, the difference-equation method, and the method of graduation by mathematical formula, all may be extended to

50

the graduation of select tables, or, generally, of series involving more than one variable. Some extensions of the theory are not in themselves very difficult; but the complication of having additional variables, and the reduction in unit volume of data because of the analysis by more than one variable, make the task of securing a satisfactory graduation of select material a much more difficult one than the graduation of a series involving only one variable.

7.2 *The select period.*

In connection with mortality data, it is usually not necessary to consider the variation by duration over its entire range. Although the effects of medical selection in connection with insured lives may never wholly disappear, in practice the difference between the select rate of mortality, $q_{[x]+t}$, and the ultimate rate of mortality, q_{x+t}, tends to disappear or become negligible after a relatively short period. This leads to the preparation of the select and ultimate type table, wherein the mortality rate varies by both duration and age only in the select years, or during the select period. Thereafter, the table runs into the ultimate portion varying only by age, in the graduation of which the data remaining after the select years are combined by attained age.

Thus, the determination of the length of the select period is usually required as a prelude to the graduation of select material. The select period is chosen as short as possible consistent with the indications of the observed data, in order that the tables be simplified as much as possible. One method is to compute the select mortality rates, $q_{[x]}$, $q_{[x]+1}$, $q_{[x]+2}$, ..., for a few years of duration, graduate the series for each duration roughly and examine the resulting rates to ascertain where the effects of selection appear to be tapering off. Another is to obtain a similar series of ultimate tables by including all but the first 10 years, all but the first 9 years, etc., of duration, and study these to see where a break may most profitably be made. A select period of 5 years, or at most 10 years, is usually found to be satisfactory.

7.3 *The first year and the ultimate years.*

The data for duration zero and for the ultimate portion of the table are usually graduated first, separately and with care. Special importance is attached to the ultimate portion of the table because, as a result of the combination of data at various ages and durations, a much greater volume of data than in the select years will be included, and because the ultimate portion of the table may be used for premium computations, reserve calculations, and so forth, to a greater extent than the select part of the table. The interest in duration zero comes in part from the fact it is the anchor from which the other select years flow into the ultimate portion of the table and in part perhaps because it represents the limit of the select effect.

7.4 *Smoothness and fit.*

In the graduation of select tables, just as in the case of graduations of functions of a single variable, a compromise is involved between the desiderata of smoothness and closeness to the observed data. The graduation must always be tested as to both of these factors. The mortality rates should flow smoothly over the select period and join smoothly with the ultimate portion of the table, which in itself should be smooth. As to fit, the observed deaths in the first year at duration zero and in the ultimate portion of the table, separately, as well as the aggregate of observed deaths for all the select and ultimate years combined, should be closely reproduced by the graduated deaths.

7.5 *Exercises.*

7.51 Define the problem of graduating select tables and discuss the select period in relation thereto.

7.52 Discuss the treatment of the data for the first year and the ultimate portion, and smoothness and fit in connection with the graduation of select tables.

CHAPTER EIGHT

General Comparison of the Methods

8.0 In the preceding chapters, different graduation methods were considered in some detail. An understandable question is whether any one is the best method. There is no best method nor is any one method better than a second in all instances. Each graduation method has its uses. There are certain situations where the use of one is definitely indicated and others where its use is inadvisable.

Each method of graduation always involves the compromise between closeness to the observed data and smoothness which, as set forth in (1.3), are the inevitable adjuncts of a graduation; the manner of the control of fit and smoothness, and of the balance between them, differs with each.

(a) In the graphic method, the graduator is free to draw the graduated curve wherever he wishes. He thus has direct control of fit. The amount of smoothness will depend on his skill in drawing a smooth curve, reading of the values, and adjusting them.

(b) In the interpolation method, the degree of fit is pretty much established by the pivotal points, while the choice of the interpolation formula affects primarily the smoothness of the results.

(c) For the adjusted-average method, the control of the relationship between fit and smoothness is in the adjusted-average formula itself. It depends upon both the range of the given formula and the pattern of its linear-compound coefficients.

(d) In the case of the difference-equation method, once the order of the difference equation is selected, the combination of smoothness and fit may be controlled directly through the value assigned to the constant of proportion h or k, appearing in the difference equation.

(e) In the applications of the method of graduation by mathematical formula, the graduated series will always have the inherent smoothness of a mathematical curve. The degree of fit will depend both on the form of the graduating curve, which may or may not be of a pattern akin to that of the observed data, and then upon the way in which the values of the constants are calculated.

8.1 *Choice of method.*

Despite the fact that one graduation method is not uniformly better than another, there are reasons in a given instance for electing to use one method instead of another. The purpose of the graduated table may not warrant the time involved in using an elaborate method. The extent of the data may be so small that the use of a more elaborate method than the graphic method is not worthwhile. Perhaps the series to be graduated consists of only a dozen terms, so that the application of a linear-compound formula would be out of the question. The graduator may not be able to draw smooth enough curves for a good graphic graduation, or he may not have the technical knowledge necessary for the Whittaker-Henderson Type B formulas.

More generally, the selection of the method to be applied in a given instance will rest upon:

  (i) The purpose to which the graduated table is to be put;

 (ii) The form in which the data are given and their general characteristics;

(iii) The extent of the data; and

(iv) The experience, technical knowledge and preference of the graduator.

These factors, of course, are not fully separable but rather are interdependent.

In any event, the acceptability of the final results of any graduation must be substantiated. In all cases, appropriate quantitative tests of fit and smoothness (articles 1.7 and 1.8) must be applied to the numerical values of the graduated series. Unless the graduated series is deemed to be satisfactory on the basis of these tests, it must be rejected regardless of the graduation method by which it is secured.

8.2 *Comparison of methods.*

The applicability of the five graduation methods under different circumstances and any advantages or disadvantages of each will now be discussed, keeping in mind the four pertinent factors mentioned in (8.1).

(a) The graphic method is an all-purpose method that may be applied easily and speedily. The method would probably not be selected in connection with an important table intended to be used for premium, reserve and similar calculations. It is particularly useful where a quick graduation is wanted for the comparison of several sets of data, in many pension fund investigations and in similar cases where the use to which the results will be put does not justify extensive mathematical processes.

The method is applicable to data of any type and shape, to data given in a number of large groups or at individual ages and to extensive as well as scanty data. Some difficulty may arise in practice from the inability to secure a scale suitable for the entire range, in drawing a smooth curve and in reading the graduated values from the diagram. Smoothness may always be improved by regraduating the graphic values by some other method. Graduation by reference to a standard table, preferably one determined by a mathematical formula, is helpful in reducing the other difficulties.

(b) The interpolation method is the only method, other than the graphic, which gives intermediate values directly where the data are given in large groups. It is primarily a method for dealing with grouped data, where intermediate values are desired, although it is always possible to use it for data given at individual ages. The method is best used where the data are sufficiently extensive so as not to require preliminary graduation to smooth them. Thus, it has found wide use in connection with population statistics.

Special formulas are required to deal with the values at the ends, which are not reached by the symmetrical formulas.

(c) Adjusted-average methods are applicable to any large experience involving a substantial number of terms to be graduated which justifies a relatively elaborate treatment. Technical knowledge and experience are required to choose an appropriate linear-compound or summation formula, but once the formula to be used has been chosen, and there are a large variety of tested formulas available, the arithmetical work may be handled by a computer without technical knowledge.

The method is not applicable to short series because a large number of terms is required to secure a graduated value. This makes the method generally inapplicable to grouped material because usually the grouping of data greatly reduces the number of terms in the ungraduated series.

Special devices are necessary at the ends, where graduated values are not given by the formulas. Accordingly, if the variation at the ends is of particular importance, as is often the case in connection with withdrawal or lapse rates, the method does not commend itself.

(d) Difference-equation methods are widely adaptable and permit a direct control of the balance between smoothness and fit. They may be used for scanty as well as extensive data. Technical knowledge is required in the choice of the appropriate formula, but once the choice has been made, the work may readily be handed to someone without such knowledge for completion.

The Type B formulas, developed for use in connection with mortality data, take account of the weight of the individual observations as an integral part of the graduation procedure. This the Type A formulas fail to do. The Type B formulas, however, require a greater degree of technical knowledge and substantially more difficult arithmetical work, which tend to restrict their use to the construction of important tables.

(e) Graduation by mathematical formula is of wide use. It is an elaborate graduation method requiring considerable technical knowledge and involving considerable work. Its use in any instance is dependent upon the knowledge of a mathematical curve of suitable form to represent the underlying series in order that a satisfactory fit may be obtained. If no such curve can be found, the method cannot be applied.

It has the definite advantage, both theoretical and practical, of having the variable expressed in terms of a mathematical formula, with the attendant inherent smoothness of a series defined by such a function. In particular, in connection with actuarial functions, the Makeham and Gompertz curves permit the applicability of the law of uniform seniority. These advantages are so substantial that, in applying the method, fidelity to the observed data is sometimes sacrificed to a greater extent than might otherwise be advisable.

The method may be applied to scanty as well as extensive data, but the purpose of the final table must justify the work of securing a satisfactory graduation.

8.3 *Mortality from infancy to the limit of life.*

An idea of the variation in l_x from infancy to the limit of life may be obtained from Figure 5a which shows the shape of the

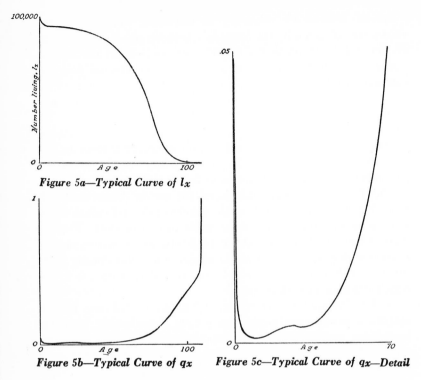

Figure 5a—Typical Curve of l_x

Figure 5b—Typical Curve of q_x Figure 5c—Typical Curve of q_x—Detail

typical l_x curve. It is seen that l_x decreases rapidly in infancy from the radix of the table and, with several points of inflexion, more slowly thereafter through the juvenile and adult ages. Finally, at the upper age limit, it flattens out to zero.

Figure 5b shows the typical variation in q_x to which the variation in each of m_x, colog p_x and μ_x is similar. This curve should be particularly noted since modern tables are based on the graduation of these functions rather than of l_x. The rate of mortality is seen to be a distorted J-shaped curve. It decreases rapidly at infancy to a minimum somewhere about age 11 and then increases slightly with a maximum sometimes appearing somewhere between ages 20 and 35. Thereafter, it increases steadily to a value of 1 at the limit of the table. The magnitude of q_x and its variation below the older ages may better be judged from Figure 5c, which is on a larger scale than Figure 5b.

Numerous attempts, mostly of historical interest, have been made to secure mathematical formulas which would represent one of the functions l_x, q_x, m_x, colog p_x or μ_x throughout. As might be expected from the pattern of the curves, none was wholly successful. The Makeham and Gompertz curves, covering a substantial range of the table, are the most successful.

A study of the methods used in the graduation of published mortality tables covering the entire span of life will generally show that the table is not graduated by means of a single graduation throughout, but is graduated in sections. This arises in part from the difficulty of dealing with the table as a whole and in part from the fact that the data are often taken from different sources.

It will be found that the curves are considered in various sections, numbering perhaps five, care being taken to see that the different sections blend smoothly with each other. The sections may comprise the infantile ages from 0 to 6, the juvenile ages 6 to 18 or so, the young adult ages from 20 to 35, the adult ages from 35 to 80 or 90, and the old ages from 80 or 90 to the limit of the table. These subdivisions are not iron-clad and in many instances will not all be present. For example, in the case of the 1941 Standard Industrial Table we find "the ungraduated adjusted death rates were used for ages 1 to 6, inclusive; Larus' 7 term symmetrical-coefficient (linear-compound) formula was applied at ages 7 to 24, inclusive; the Whittaker-Henderson 'A' formula minimizing third differences and with a equal to 2 ($k = 22.02$) was applied at ages 25 to 82, inclusive, and for ages 83 to 98, inclusive, the rates obtained by the Makeham extension were used without further modification other than the addition of the constant margin. The limiting age was taken as age 99."

8.4 *The function to be graduated.*

The choice of the function to be graduated is, to some extent, within the control of the graduator. It is preferable, because the graduation is thereby made easier, that as far as possible maxima and minima, points of inflexion, and other singularities be avoided. To that end, it is often desirable to transform the function to be graduated so as to eliminate them or reduce their importance. It may also be helpful to reduce the range of variation of the function to be graduated.

King advocated the graduation of the function log ($q_x + .1$). The use of ratios to a standard table was referred to in (2.3) in connection with the graphic method. It should be noted that the advantages of their use are not confined to that method.

8.5 *Modern tables.*

Tables suitable for valuation, non-forfeiture values, premiums and so forth, must provide adequate margins for mortality fluctuations and contingencies. In the past, such margins were secured by using for such purposes tables based upon data of prior years. Such tables showed higher mortality rates than those being experienced, or expected to be experienced, during the period when they were to be employed and, therefore, were satisfactory for valuation, non-forfeiture values, etc.

The construction of the 1941 Industrial Tables and the 1941 Commissioners Standard Ordinary Table was based on a different principle. Tables based upon current mortality experience, but appropriate for use as standards for valuation and so forth, were to be constructed. The necessary margins for mortality fluctuations and contingencies were inserted directly into the tables as a part of their construction. Thus, for the 1941 Standard Industrial Table adjusted death rates were calculated so that the rates actually experienced would be 80% of such rates. For the 1941 Commissioners Standard Ordinary Table, a margin of five per cent of the reciprocal of the expectation of life was added to the experience rates of mortality. In the construction of such tables, the final table is obtained by the graduation of the adjusted mortality rates which are substituted for the observed values.

8.6 *Exercises.*

8.61 Compare the methods of graduation including any advantages or disadvantages of each under different circumstances and name one table to which each method was applied.

8.62 For each graduation method, give the particular objections, if any, to its use for graduating data of the following types:

    (a) Lapse rates under life insurance policies;

    (b) Aggregate disability rates under policies issued with the 90 day clause;

    (c) Ultimate mortality rates under immediate life annuities issued at adult ages by a large life insurance company;

    (d) Accidental death rates;

    (e) Mortality rates among married women;

    (f) Rates of retirement under a large pension plan;

    (g) Records of population and deaths by age obtained from census statistics;

    (h) Rates of marriage among bachelors.

8.63 The exposed to risk, deaths and crude mortality rates for age group at entry 60-64 are given below. Also given are the results of three graduations of these data. State the criteria that you would apply to determine whether these results are satisfactory. Apply these criteria to the graduation by the Whittaker-Henderson Formula A. State which method of graduation you consider most suitable to data of this character, giving your reasons.

Year of Exposure	Exposed to Risk	Deaths	Crude Death Rates	Whittaker-Henderson Formula A	Graphic Method	Makeham's Formula
1	190,000	2,660	.014	.014	.013	.014
2	150,000	2,850	.019	.018	.019	.017
3	110,000	1,870	.017	.021	.021	.020
4	85,000	2,125	.025	.024	.024	.024
5	61,000	1,647	.027	.027	.028	.028
6	44,000	1,364	.031	.031	.032	.032
7	33,000	1,155	.035	.036	.036	.037
8	24,000	1,104	.046	.040	.040	.042
9	15,000	855	.057	.045	.046	.048
10	10,000	450	.045	.049	.051	.054
11	6,000	216	.036	.056	.058	.061
12	2,000	186	.093	.066	.065	.069

8.64 The following table shows two graduations of certain crude rates of mortality. State, with reasons, which of these graduations you think is superior. What special problems do you think were involved in graduating these crude rates?

Age	Exposed	Actual Deaths	Crude Rate	Graduation I	Graduation II
70	135	6	.044	.056	.050
71	143	12	.084	.060	.055
72	129	10	.078	.067	.062
73	150	11	.073	.073	.070
74	150	6	.040	.080	.080
75	150	16	.107	.087	.090
76	150	24	.160	.094	.103
77	139	8	.058	.103	.115
78	145	16	.110	.112	.126
79	140	13	.093	.122	.139
80	137	19	.139	.133	.152
Total	1,568	141			

CHAPTER NINE

Data for Illustrative Numerical Exercises

9.0 The data for the numerical problems illustrating the graduation methods are based on actual experience. If the student feels the need for further numerical examples, he may draw upon the reports published in the Transactions by the Joint Committee on Mortality and the experience of his company for additional data as he sees fit.

9.1 *Experience under refund annuities issued to women by number of contracts.*

Contract Year	Exposed to Risk	Actual Deaths	Expected Deaths	Ratio of Act. to Exp.
1	9,839	128	211.35	61%
2	8,411	164	197.34	83
3	12,443	266	304.06	87
4	10,782	279	277.40	101
5	12,142	311	339.20	92
6	13,992	450	402.30	112
7	14,106	384	414.31	93
8	7,431	213	223.09	95
9	2,876	93	90.09	103
10	1,417	46	47.41	97
Total	93,439	2,334	2,506.55	93%

The expected deaths are by the 1937 Standard Annuity Table. From *T.A.S.A. XLIII*, page 147.

9.2 *Experience under standard "ordinary" insurance issues.*

Attained Ages	Exposed to Risk	Actual Deaths	Rate of Mortality Per M	Expected Deaths	Ratio of Act. to Exp.
25-29	35,700	139	3.91	114	122%
30-34	244,066	599	2.45	990	61
35-39	741,041	1,842	2.49	3,905	47
40-44	1,250,601	4,771	3.81	8,933	53
45-49	1,746,393	11,073	6.34	17,540	63
50-54	2,067,008	21,693	10.50	29,794	73
55-59	1,983,710	31,612	15.94	41,743	76
60-64	1,484,347	39,948	26.91	46,137	87
65-69	988,980	40,295	40.74	45,637	88
70-74	559,049	33,292	59.55	38,380	87
75-79	241,497	20,773	86.02	24,508	85
80-84	78,229	11,376	145.41	11,622	98
85-89	15,411	2,653	172.18	3,312	80
90-94	2,552	589	230.77	791	74
95-	162	44	270.24	64	69
Total	11,438,746	220,699		273,470	81%

The unit is $1,000 of insurance and the expected deaths are by the Commissioners 1941 Standard Ordinary Table for individual attained ages. From *T.A.S.A. XLV*, page 415.

9.3 *Experience under standard "ordinary" insurance issues of a large company.*

The unit is $1,000 of insurance and the expected deaths are calculated by the Commissioners 1941 Standard Ordinary Table.

At-tained Age	Crude Rate of Mortality	q_x by C.S.O. Table	Exposed to Risk	Actual Deaths	Expected Deaths	Ratio of Act. to Exp.
35	.00215	.00459	12,118	26	55.6	47%
36	.00212	.00486	15,115	32	73.5	44
37	.00169	.00515	18,392	31	94.7	33
38	.00192	.00546	22,346	43	122.0	35
39	.00320	.00581	26,210	84	152.3	55
40	.00238	.00618	29,035	69	179.4	38
41	.00259	.00659	30,890	80	203.6	39
42	.00553	.00703	34,723	192	244.1	79
43	.00311	.00751	36,007	112	270.4	41
44	.00365	.00804	40,861	149	328.5	45
45	.00446	.00861	41,259	184	355.2	52
46	.00632	.00923	46,040	291	424.9	68
47	.00741	.00991	44,534	330	441.3	75
48	.00726	.01064	48,060	349	511.4	68
49	.00945	.01145	51,343	485	587.9	82
50	.00749	.01232	53,261	399	656.2	61
51	.00763	.01327	52,689	402	699.2	57
52	.01064	.01430	54,977	585	786.2	74
53	.00999	.01543	56,130	561	866.1	65
54	.01378	.01665	53,121	732	884.5	83
55	.00967	.01798	51,909	502	933.3	54
56	.01826	.01943	51,034	932	991.6	94
57	.01811	.02100	52,071	943	1,093.5	86
58	.01593	.02271	46,020	733	1,045.1	70
59	.01789	.02457	45,106	807	1,108.3	73
60	.01853	.02659	40,480	750	1,076.4	70
61	.03246	.02878	38,235	1,241	1,100.4	113
62	.02794	.03118	38,374	1,072	1,196.5	90
63	.01937	.03376	37,065	718	1,251.3	57
64	.04000	.03658	33,699	1,348	1,232.7	109
65	.02795	.03964	30,199	844	1,197.1	71
66	.03764	.04296	28,399	1,069	1,220.0	88
67	.04123	.04656	25,223	1,040	1,174.4	89
68	.03459	.05046	24,138	835	1,218.0	69
69	.05391	.05470	21,943	1,183	1,200.3	99
70	.05721	.05930	19,351	1,107	1,147.5	96
71	.06504	.06427	16,359	1,064	1,051.4	101
72	.04564	.06966	15,864	724	1,105.1	66
73	.05975	.07550	13,221	790	998.2	79
74	.06535	.08181	11,355	742	929.0	80
75	.06652	.08864	9,892	658	876.8	75
76	.08061	.09602	7,890	636	757.6	84
77	.11921	.10399	6,241	744	649.0	115
78	.08340	.11259	6,163	514	693.9	74
79	.12115	.12186	4,515	547	550.2	99
Total			1,441,857	26,679	33,734.6	79%

CHAPTER TEN

Appendix

10.0 The appendix is intended to supplement the presentation in the text of the Monograph and to permit the student to secure a somewhat more complete understanding of the subject, if he wishes.

10.1 *King's formulas* **(3.3).**

King's formulas provide a method of computing the pivotal value u_x from the quinquennial sums into which the data are assumed to be grouped. Denoting the quinquennial sums by w_x,

we have $w_x = u_{x-2} + u_{x-1} + u_x + u_{x+1} + u_{x+2}$. Defining y_x as $\sum_0^{x-1} u_t$,

we then have $u_x = y_{x+1} - y_x$ and $w_x = y_{x+3} - y_{x-2}$. By the Gauss central difference formula (3.41) with Δ referring to 5 year intervals,

$$y_{x+t} = y_{x-2} + \frac{t+2}{5}\Delta y_{x-2} + \frac{(t+2)}{5}\frac{(t-3)}{5}\frac{\Delta^2 y_{x-7}}{2!}$$
$$+ \frac{(t+2)}{5}\frac{(t-3)}{5}\frac{(t+7)\Delta^3 y_{x-7}}{5}\frac{1}{3!} \qquad (10.11)$$
$$+ \frac{(t+2)}{5}\frac{(t-3)}{5}\frac{(t+7)}{5}\frac{(t-8)}{5}\frac{\Delta^4 y_{x-12}}{4!} + \cdots.$$

Hence

$$y_{x+1} = y_{x-2} + .6\Delta y_{x-2} - .12\Delta^2 y_{x-7} - .064\Delta^3 y_{x-7} + .0224\Delta^4 y_{x-12}$$
$$+ .011648\Delta^5 y_{x-12} + \cdots,$$
$$y_x = y_{x-2} + .4\Delta y_{x-2} - .12\Delta^2 y_{x-7} - .056\Delta^3 y_{x-7} + .0224\Delta^4 y_{x-12}$$
$$+ .010752\Delta^5 y_{x-12} + \cdots.$$

Thus

$$y_{x+1} - y_x = .2\Delta y_{x-2} - .008\Delta^3 y_{x-7} + .000896\Delta^5 y_{x-12} + \cdots,$$

or

$$u_x = .2w_x - .008(w_{x-5} - 2w_x + w_{x+5}), \qquad (10.12)$$

for King's formula correct to third differences, and

$$u_x = .2w_x - .008(w_{x-5} - 2w_x + w_{x+5})$$
$$+ .000896 \ (w_{x-10} - 4w_{x-5} + 6w_x - 4w_{x+5} + w_{x+10}),$$
$$(10.13)$$

for King's formula correct to fifth differences.

10.2 *The Karup-King formula* (3.42).

The Karup-King formula for interpolating in the interval x to $x+1$ is based upon the four pivotal points u_{x-1}, u_x, u_{x+1} and u_{x+2}. The conditions underlying the formula require that

   (i) The interpolating curve shall pass through the pivotal points u_x and u_{x+1};

  (ii) The interpolating curve shall have the same tangent at u_x as the parabola through the pivotal points u_{x-1}, u_x and u_{x+1} and the same tangent at u_{x+1} as the parabola through the pivotal points u_x, u_{x+1} and u_{x+2}.

Let the interpolated value u_{x+s} be given in Everett form by

$$u_{x+s} = A(s)u_{x+1} + B(s)\,\delta^2 u_{x+1}$$
$$+ A(1-s)u_x + B(1-s)\,\delta^2 u_x, \qquad (10.21)$$

where $A(s)$ and $B(s)$ are functions of s of minimum degree to be determined by conditions (i) and (ii). Differentiating (10.21) with respect to s gives

$$u'_{x+s} = A'(s)u_{x+1} + B'(s)\,\delta^2 u_{x+1}$$
$$- A'(1-s)u_x - B'(1-s)\,\delta^2 u_x. \qquad (10.22)$$

Now, the parabola through the pivotal points u_{x-1}, u_x and u_{x+1} is, by Gauss' formula (3.41),

$$y_{x+s} = u_x + s\Delta u_x + \frac{s(s-1)}{2}\delta^2 u_x \qquad (10.23)$$

and its first derivative with respect to s is

$$y'_{x+s} = \Delta u_x + \frac{2s-1}{2}\delta^2 u_x. \qquad (10.24)$$

For the parabola through the pivotal points u_x, u_{x+1} and u_{x+2}, $x+1$ replaces x in equations (10.23) and (10.24).

Imposing condition (i), first at $x(s=0)$ and then at $x+1$ $(s=1)$, we have, by (10.21),

$$u_x = A(0)u_{x+1} + A(1)u_x + B(0)\,\delta^2 u_{x+1} + B(1)\,\delta^2 u_x \qquad (10.25a)$$

and $\;u_{x+1} = A(1)u_{x+1} + A(0)u_x + B(1)\,\delta^2 u_{x+1} + B(0)\,\delta^2 u_x.$ (10.25b)

Condition (ii) becomes the basis of another two equations. By equating (10.22) with $s=0$ to (10.24) with $s=0$, we have at x

$$[A'(0)-1]u_{x+1} - [A'(1)-1]u_x + B'(0)\,\delta^2 u_{x+1} + [\tfrac{1}{2}-B'(1)]\delta^2 u_x = 0,$$
$$(10.26a)$$

At $x+1$, by equating (10.22) with $s=1$ to (10.24) with $s=0$ and x replaced by $x+1$, we obtain after simplification,

$$[A'(1)-1]u_{x+1} - [A'(0)-1]u_x - B'(0)\;\delta^2 u_x - [\tfrac{1}{2}-B'(1)]\delta^2 u_{x+1} = 0.$$
$$(10.26b)$$

Now, the functions $A(s)$ and $B(s)$ are to be completely independent of the numerical values of u_x, u_{x+1}, $\delta^2 u_x$ and $\delta^2 u_{x+1}$. Accordingly, by equations (10.25), $A(s)$ must be such that $A(0)=0$ and $A(1)=1$, and from equations (10.26), $A'(0)=A'(1)=1$. Thus, $A(s)$ is determined to be equal to s. Similarly, $B(0)=B(1)=B'(0)=0$ and $B'(1)=\tfrac{1}{2}$, and $B(s)=-\dfrac{s^2(1-s)}{2}$. Finally, we have for the Karup-King formula:

$$u_{x+s} = su_{x+1} - \frac{s^2(1-s)}{2}\,\delta^2 u_{x+1}$$
$$\qquad\qquad (10.27)$$
$$+(1-s)u_x - \frac{(1-s)^2[1-(1-s)]}{2}\,\delta^2 u_x.$$

10.3 *Shovelton's formula* (3.43).

Shovelton's formula for interpolating in the interval x to $x+1$ is based on the six pivotal points $u_{x-2}, u_{x-1}, u_x, u_{x+1}, u_{x+2}$ and u_{x+3}. It satisfies the conditions that:

  (i) The interpolating curve shall pass through the pivotal points u_x and u_{x+1};

  (ii) The interpolating curve shall have the same tangent at u_x as the curve through the pivotal points $u_{x-2}, u_{x-1}, u_x, u_{x+1}$ and u_{x+2} and the same tangent at u_{x+1} as the curve through the pivotal points $u_{x-1}, u_x, u_{x+1}, u_{x+2}$ and u_{x+3};

  (iii) In the interval x to $x+1$, the area under the interpolating curve shall be equal to the mean of the areas under the two curves mentioned in condition (ii).

The formula was presented by S. T. Shovelton in *J.I.A. XLVII*, p. 284. It was designed not only to be tangential but also, by means of condition (iii), to reproduce approximately the area included by the crude values in the interval of interpolation. The proof of the formula, while similar to that of the Karup-King formula (10.2), is considerably longer and more involved.

10.4 *Jenkins' modified osculatory formula* (3.51).

The Jenkins' fifth-difference modified osculatory formula for the interval x to $x+1$ is based upon the six pivotal points u_{x-2}, u_{x-1}, u_x, u_{x+1}, u_{x+2} and u_{x+3}. The conditions underlying the formula are that

(i) At the point x, the interpolating curve functions for the adjoining intervals $x-1$ to x and x to $x+1$ shall have the same value, i.e., they shall meet, and their first and second derivatives, respectively, shall be equal;

(ii) When the five pivotal points u_{x-2}, u_{x-1}, u_x, u_{x+1} and u_{x+2}, lie on the same 3rd degree curve, the point of coincidence of the interpolating curves at x shall be the pivotal point u_x.

This formula is one of the family of modified osculatory formulas of varying orders of differences that may be derived by suitably modifying the above conditions.

Suppose the interpolating function in the interval x to $x+1$ to be given in Everett form by

$$u_{x+s} = A(s)u_{x+1} + B(s)\,\delta^2 u_{x+1} + C(s)\,\delta^4 u_{x+1}$$
$$+ A(1-s)u_x + B(1-s)\,\delta^2 u_x + C(1-s)\,\delta^4 u_x, \tag{10.41}$$

where $A(s)$, $B(s)$ and $C(s)$ are functions of s of minimum degree to be determined by the above conditions.

Setting (10.41) with $s=0$ equal to (10.41) with $s=1$ and x replaced by $x-1$, it follows in accordance with condition (i) that

$$A(0)(u_{x+1}-u_{x-1}) + B(0)(\delta^2 u_{x+1} - \delta^2 u_{x-1})$$
$$+ C(0)(\delta^4 u_{x+1} - \delta^4 u_{x-1}) = 0, \tag{10.42}$$

whence we must have $A(0) = B(0) = C(0) = 0$.

Setting the first derivative of (10.41) with $s=0$ equal to the first derivative of (10.41) with $s=1$ and x replaced by $x-1$, we obtain

$$A'(0)(u_{x+1}+u_{x-1}) - A'(1)(2u_x)$$
$$+ B'(0)(\delta^2 u_{x+1} + \delta^2 u_{x-1}) - B'(1)(2\,\delta^2 u_x)$$
$$+ C'(0)(\delta^4 u_{x+1} + \delta^4 u_{x-1}) - C'(1)(2\,\delta^4 u_x) = 0,$$

or, rearranging,

$$2[A'(0)-A'(1)]u_x+[2B'(0)-2B'(1)+A'(0)]\delta^2 u_x$$
$$+C'(0)[\delta^4 u_{x+1}+\delta^4 u_{x-1}]+[B'(0)-2C'(1)]\delta^4 u_x=0, \quad (10.43)$$

whence $A'(0)=A'(1)$, $2B'(0)-2B'(1)+A'(0)=0$, $C'(0)=0$ and $B'(0)=2C'(1)$.

Setting the second derivative of (10.41) with $s=0$ equal to the second derivative of (10.41) with $s=1$ and x replaced by $x-1$, we must have

$$A''(0)(u_{x+1}-u_{x-1})+B''(0)(\delta^2 u_{x+1}-\delta^2 u_{x-1})$$
$$+C''(0)(\delta^4 u_{x+1}-\delta^4 u_{x-1})=0, \quad (10.44)$$

whence $A''(0)=B''(0)=C''(0)=0$.

Finally, applying condition (ii), we must have when $\delta^4 u_x=0$

$$u_x=A(0)u_{x+1}+B(0)\,\delta^2 u_{x+1}+C(0)\,\delta^4 u_{x+1}$$
$$+A(1)u_x+B(1)\,\delta^2 u_x+C(1)\,\delta^4 u_x, \quad (10.45)$$

whence $A(1)=1$ and $B(1)=0$.

The function of minimum degree satisfying the conditions, $A(0)=A''(0)=0$ and $A(1)=1$, is $A(s)=s$. Consequently, $A'(0)=1$, and the function of minimum degree satisfying the conditions $B(0)=B(1)=B''(0)=0$ and $2B'(0)-2B'(1)+1=0$ is $B(s)=\dfrac{s(s^2-1)}{6}$. Accordingly, $B'(0)=-\frac{1}{6}$, and the function of minimum degree satisfying $C(0)=C'(0)=C''(0)=0$ and $2C'(1)+\frac{1}{6}=0$ is $C(s)=\dfrac{-s^3}{36}$.

We thus have for the Jenkins' fifth-difference modified osculatory formula:

$$u_{x+s}=su_{x+1}+\frac{s(s^2-1)}{6}\,\delta^2 u_{x+1}-\frac{s^3}{36}\delta^4 u_{x+1}$$
$$+(1-s)u_x+\frac{(1-s)[(1-s)^2-1]}{6}\delta^2 u_x-\frac{(1-s)^3}{36}\,\delta^4 u_x. \quad (10.46)$$

Equation (3.51) is a rearrangement of the terms of (10.46) made for ease of computation.

10.5 *Linear-compound formulas with minimum R_0 (maximum Weight).*

If a linear-compound formula is to effect a maximum reduction in the mean square error of the terms of the ungraduated series, then its coefficients must be such that R_0 is a minimum. Thus, the expression

$$S = a_0{}^2 + 2\sum_1^n a_r{}^2 \qquad (10.51)$$

is to be a minimum, subject to the two conditions arising from the requirement that the application of the graduation formula to a third-degree function reproduce it without change:

$$1 = a_0 + 2\sum_1^n a_r, \qquad (10.52a)$$

$$0 = \sum_1^n r^2 a_r. \qquad (10.52b)$$

Now, each of the coefficients is a variable independent of each other. Solving equations (10.52) for a_0 and a_1 in terms of the remaining coefficients, gives

$$a_1 = -\sum_2^n r^2 a_r, \qquad (10.53a)$$

$$a_0 = 1 + 2\sum_2^n (r^2 - 1)a_r. \qquad (10.53b)$$

Then, considering S to be a function of the $r-1$ independent variables a_r and the two dependent variables a_1 and a_0, in order for S to be a minimum, we must have

$$\frac{dS}{da_r} = \frac{\partial S}{\partial a_r} + \frac{\partial S}{\partial a_1}\frac{da_1}{da_r} + \frac{\partial S}{\partial a_0}\frac{da_0}{da_r} = 0. \qquad (10.54)$$

From equations (10.53), $\dfrac{da_1}{da_r} = -r^2$ and $\dfrac{da_0}{da_r} = 2(r^2 - 1)$, and from

equation (10.51) $\dfrac{\partial S}{\partial a_r} = 4a_r, \dfrac{\partial S}{\partial a_1} = 4a_1, \dfrac{\partial S}{\partial a_0} = 2a_0.$ Substituting in (10.54), gives

$$4a_r - 4r^2 a_1 + 4(r^2 - 1)a_0 = 0,$$

or

$$a_r = a_0 + r^2(a_1 - a_0). \qquad (10.55)$$

This equation holds for all values of r from 0 to n. Letting r take on successively the values 1, 2, . . . , n, in (10.55) and summing the resultant equations gives

$$\sum_{1}^{n} a_r = s_2(a_1 - a_0) + na_0, \qquad (10.56a)$$

where $\sum_{1}^{n} r^t$ is denoted by s_t. Similarly, after first multiplying by r^2, we have

$$\sum_{1}^{n} r^2 a_r = s_4(a_1 - a_0) + s_2 a_0. \qquad (10.56b)$$

Substituting in equations (10.52), we have

$$\begin{cases} 1 = a_0(1+2n) + 2s_2(a_1 - a_0), \\ 0 = s_4(a_1 - a_0) + s_2 a_0. \end{cases} \qquad (10.57)$$

Substituting $s_2 = \frac{1}{6} n(n+1)(2n+1)$ and $\frac{s_4}{s_2} = \frac{1}{5}(3n^2 + 3n - 1)$ and solving gives

$$a_1 - a_0 = \frac{-15}{(2n+3)(2n+1)(2n-1)}$$

and

$$a_0 = \frac{3(3n^2 + 3n - 1)}{(2n+3)(2n+1)(2n-1)},$$

or

$$a_r = \frac{3(3n^2 + 3n - 1) - 15r^2}{(2n-1)(2n+1)(2n+3)}, \qquad (10.58)$$

from which the coefficients may be successively calculated for any given value of n by letting $r = 0, 1, 2, \ldots, n$.

10.6 *Linear-compound formulas with minimum R_3 (minimum smoothing coefficient).*

If a linear-compound formula is to effect a maximum reduction in the mean square error in the third differences of the terms of the ungraduated series, its coefficients must be such that R_3 is a minimum. Consequently,

$$S = \sum_{-n-3}^{n} (\Delta^3 a_r)^2 \qquad (10.61)$$

must be a minimum, subject to the two equations (10.52) or (10.53). The proof is similar to that in (10.5) and may be found on pages 58-60 of Mathematical Theory of Graduation (Actuarial Studies No. 4) by R. Henderson. The coefficients a_r turn out to be

$$a_r = \frac{315\,[(m-1)^2-r^2]\,[m^2-r^2]\,[(m+1)^2-r^2]\,[(3m^2-16)-11r^2]}{8m(m^2-1)(4m^2-1)(4m^2-9)(4m^2-25)},$$

(10.62)

where $m=n+2$.

10.7 *Factorization of the difference equation.*

The fourth-order difference equation $u_x''=u_x+h\,\delta^4 u_x$ may also be written as

$$u_x''=(1+h\Delta^4 E^{-2})u_x.$$

(10.71)

From the symmetry of the equation, it seems reasonable to express the factors initially as $(1-a\Delta+b\Delta^2)$ and $(1+a\Delta E^{-1}+b\Delta^2 E^{-2})$, where a and b must then satisfy the identity:

$$1+h\Delta^4 E^{-2}=(1-a\Delta+b\Delta^2)(1+a\Delta E^{-1}+b\Delta^2 E^{-2}),$$

or

$$1+h\Delta^4 E^{-2}=1+a\Delta(E^{-1}-1)+b\Delta^2(E^{-2}+1)-a^2\Delta^2 E^{-1}$$
$$-ab\Delta^3 E^{-1}(E^{-1}-1)+b^2\Delta^4 E^{-2}.$$

Since $E^{-1}-1=-\Delta E^{-1}$ and $E^{-2}+1=2E^{-1}+\Delta^2 E^{-2}$, this becomes

$$h\Delta^4 E^{-2}=(-a-a^2+2b)\Delta^2 E^{-1}+(b+ab+b^2)\Delta^4 E^{-2},$$

whence,

$$-a-a^2+2b=0,\ \text{or}\ b=a\frac{(a+1)}{2},$$

and

$$h=b(1+a+b),$$

so that

$$h=\frac{a(a+1)^2(a+2)}{4}.$$

(10.72)

The fourth-order difference equation is thus equivalent to the two second-order difference equations

$$u_x''=[1+a\Delta E^{-1}+a\frac{(a+1)}{2}\Delta^2 E^{-2}]u_x'$$
$$=u_x'+a\Delta u_{x-1}'+a\frac{(a+1)}{2}\Delta^2 u_{x-2}',$$

(10.73a)

$$u_x'=[1-a\Delta+a\frac{(a+1)}{2}\Delta^2]u_x$$
$$=u_x-a\Delta u_x+a\frac{(a+1)}{2}\Delta^2 u_x,$$

(10.73b)

where u'_x is an intermediate series. The equivalent equations

$$u''_x = \frac{(a+1)(a+2)}{2}u'_x - a(a+2)u'_{x-1} + a\frac{(a+1)}{2}u'_{x-2}, \quad (10.74a)$$

$$u'_x = \frac{(a+1)(a+2)}{2}u_x - a(a+2)u_{x+1} + a\frac{(a+1)}{2}u_{x+2} \quad (10.74b)$$

are obtained by expanding the differences.

10.8 *Starting values.*

The derivation of the difference equation (5.21) is not given in complete detail in (5.1) and (5.2). Where the graduated series q_x will consist of $\omega+1$ terms from 0 to ω, the minimizing of the expression

$$F + hS = \sum_0^\omega (q_x - q''_x)^2 + h\sum_0^{\omega-2}(\Delta^2 q_x)^2$$

leads to a series of equations, one for each value of x. All have the same form except the first two equations and the last two, which are atypical because second differences for $x = -1, -2, \omega-1$, and ω do not exist and are not present in $F + hS$. In terms of u_x, the $\omega+1$ equations are

$$\begin{aligned}
&(u_0 - u''_0) + h(\Delta^2 u_0) = 0, \\
&(u_1 - u''_1) + h(-2\Delta^2 u_0 + \Delta^2 u_1) = 0, \\
&(u_x - u''_x) + h(\Delta^2 u_{x-2} - 2\Delta^2 u_{x-1} + \Delta^2 u_x) = 0, \quad \text{for } 2 \leq x \leq \omega - 2 \\
&(u_{\omega-1} - u''_{\omega-1}) + h(\Delta^2 u_{\omega-3} - 2\Delta^2 u_{\omega-2}) = 0, \qquad\qquad (10.81) \\
&(u_\omega - u''_\omega) + h(\Delta^2 u_{\omega-2}) = 0.
\end{aligned}$$

The equations (10.81) may be made to assume the same form so that the difference equation

$$u''_x = u_x + h\delta^4 u_x \qquad (10.82)$$

will hold generally if the graduated and ungraduated series are considered to be extended by the addition of terms for $x = -2, -1, \omega+1$ and $\omega+2$. Furthermore, if the terms added are made subject to the conditions that

    (i) each graduated value equals its corresponding ungraduated value, and

    (ii) the graduated second differences $\Delta^2 u_{-2}$, $\Delta^2 u_{-1}$, $\Delta^2 u_{\omega-1}$ and $\Delta^2 u_\omega$ all vanish,

the graduated series u_x will remain the one for which $F + hS$ is a minimum, since the additions to F and S are all zero.

At the ω end, by condition (ii), we have $u_{\omega+1}=2u_\omega-u_{\omega-1}$ and $u_{\omega+2}=2u_{\omega+1}-u_\omega=3u_\omega-2u_{\omega-1}$. By substitution in (10.74b), we find

$$\begin{aligned} u'_{\omega-1} &= (a+1)u_{\omega-1}-au_\omega, \\ u'_\omega &= au_{\omega-1}-(a-1)u_\omega. \end{aligned} \tag{10.83}$$

Solving for $u_{\omega-1}$ and u_ω, we obtain equations (5.35).

At the other end, by condition (ii), $u_{-1}=2u_0-u_1$ and $u_{-2}=2u_{-1}-u_0=3u_0-2u_1$, and by substitution in (10.74b), we have

$$\begin{aligned} u'_{-2} &= (a+3)u_0-(a+2)u_1=u_0-(a+2)\Delta u_0, \\ u'_{-1} &= (a+2)u_0-(a+1)u_1=u_1-(a+2)\Delta u_0, \end{aligned} \tag{10.84}$$

which, expressed in terms of the estimated graduated values u^*_0 and u^*_1 become equations (5.36). From equations (10.84), the terms u'_{-2} and u'_{-1} are seen to lie on the straight line through the graduated values u_0 and u_1. That is the reason for using a straight line drawn among the last four or five terms of the ungraduated series to estimate the unavailable graduated terms. In effect, an attempt is made to estimate the position of the straight line from the indications of the ungraduated series.

The terms $u_{\omega-1}$ and u_ω lie on the straight line through $u'_{\omega-1}$ and u'_ω but, as distinguished from the situation at the other end, the last two calculated values of the intermediate series fully determine the position of that line.

10.9 *Correction of starting values.*

Equations (5.37) and their derivation were developed for the purposes of the Monograph by C. A. Spoerl.

Let the transformation by which one passes from u_0 and u_1 to u'_{-2} and u'_{-1}:

$$\begin{cases} u'_{-2}=(a+3)u_0-(a+2)u_1 \\ u'_{-1}=(a+2)u_0-(a+1)u_1 \end{cases} \tag{10.91}$$

be designated by T. Let G be the graduation process, from u'_{-2} and u'_{-1} down the u'_x column, up the u_x column, resulting in the graduated values u_0 and u_1. Then, (TG) is the whole process from u^*_0 and u^*_1 to u_0 and u_1.

Now let X and Y be corrections, respectively, to u_0 and u_1 to produce true values. Then

$$TG(u_0+X, u_1+Y) = (u_0+X, u_1+Y).$$

But
$$TG(u^*_0, u^*_1) = (u_0, u_1).$$

Hence
$$TG'\ (u_0-u^*_0+X, u_1-u^*_1+Y) = (X, Y), \qquad (10.92)$$

where G' refers to a graduation with all u''_x terms zero.

If, now, an infinite range is assumed, X and Y can be found explicitly in terms of $(u_0-u^*_0)$ and $(u_1-u^*_1)$.

For one infinite set, the one corresponding to the ungraduated series, $\ldots$, 0, 0, 0, 1, 0, 0, 0, $\ldots$, the three columns of the graduation look like this:

(1) x	(2) u''_x	(3) u'_x	(4) u_x
.	.	.	.
.	.	.	.
.	.	.	.
-3	0	0	k_3
-2	0	0	k_2
-1	0	0	k_1
0	1	s	k_0
1	0	sp	k_1
2	0	$s(p^2-q)$	k_2
3	0	$s(p^3-2pq)$	k_3
.	.	.	.
.	.	.	.
.	.	.	.

Here, $s=\dfrac{2}{(a+1)(a+2)}$, $p=\dfrac{2a}{(a+1)}$ and $q=\dfrac{a}{(a+2)}$ and equations (10.74) have the form

$$su''_x = u'_x - pu'_{x-1} + qu'_{x-2} \qquad (10.93a)$$
$$su'_x = u_x - pu_{x+1} + qu_{x+2}. \qquad (10.93b)$$

It is not necessary to find the k's; the essential thing is to note from (10.93b) that designating k_{-x} by k_x

$$k_x = pk_{x-1} - qk_{x-2} \qquad (10.94)$$

for the entire upper half of the last column, i.e., for the values of k corresponding to $x=0$, -1, -2, -3, $\ldots$. Since, by virtue of the symmetry of the ungraduated series, the k's are symmetrical, this holds for the lower half as well. In other words, any three successive k's are connected by the relationship (10.94). (The student may refer to "Whittaker-Henderson Graduation Formula A" by C. A. Spoerl, *T.A.S.A. XXXVIII*, page 418 ff., for further information regarding the nature and determination of the k's.)

In order to see how corresponding values of u'_x and u_x are related under G', the relationship among the k's may be combined with

$$u'_x = pu'_{x-1} - qu'_{x-2} \tag{10.95}$$

to develop the following table. The steps are numbered. The procedure is first to let $u_0 = 1$ and $u_1 = 0$. Then, by means of (10.94) compute u_2 and u_{-1}. Equation (10.93b) is used for steps (5) and (6) and equation (10.95) for step (7).

(1) x	(2) u''_x	(3) u'_x		(4) u_x	
.	.	.		.	
.	.	.		.	
.	.	.		.	
-2	0	$\dfrac{(1-q)\,(p^2-q-q^2)}{q^2 s}$	(7)	.	
-1	0	$\dfrac{p(1-q)}{qs}$	(6)	$\dfrac{p}{q}$	(4)
0	0	$\dfrac{1-q^2}{s}$	(5)	1	(1)
1	0	.		0	(2)
2	0	.		$-q$	(3)
.	.	.		.	
.	.	.		.	

It is seen that under G', the u'_{-2} and u'_{-1} corresponding to $u_0 = 1$ and $u_1 = 0$ are

$$u'_{-2} = \frac{(1-q)}{qs}\frac{(p^2-q-q^2)}{q} \text{ and } u'_{-1} = \frac{(1-q)(p)}{qs}.$$

Similarly, under G', the u'_{-2} and u'_{-1} corresponding to $u_0 = 0$ and $u_1 = 1$ are

$$u'_{-2} = \frac{(1-q)}{qs}\frac{(-p)}{q} \text{ and } u'_{-1} = -\frac{(1-q)(1+q)}{qs}.$$

The two pairs of u''s work out, respectively, as

$$u'_{-2} = 2\frac{(a^3 + 5a^2 + 5a - 1)}{(a+1)(a)}, \ u'_{-1} = 2(a+2)$$

and

$$u'_{-2} = -2\frac{(a+2)^2}{a}, \ u'_{-1} = -2\frac{(a+1)^2}{a}.$$

By applying the inverse of T,

$$\begin{cases} u_0 = -(a+1)u'_{-2} + (a+2)u'_{-1}, \\ u_1 = -(a+2)u'_{-2} + (a+3)u'_{-1}, \end{cases} \tag{10.96}$$

to these values, we find for the first pair,

$$u^\alpha_0 = -\frac{2}{a}(a^2 + a - 1), \ u^\alpha_1 = -\frac{2(a+2)}{a(a+1)}(a^2 + 2a - 1);$$

and for the second pair,

$$u^\beta_0 = \frac{2}{a}(a+1)(a+2), \ u^\beta_1 = \frac{2}{a}(a^2 + 5a + 5).$$

This means that

$$TG'(u^\alpha_0, u^\alpha_1) = (1,0),$$

and

$$TG'(u^\beta_0, u^\beta_1) = (0,1).$$

Hence

$$TG'(Xu^\alpha_0 + Yu^\beta_0, Xu^\alpha_1 + Yu^\beta_1) = (X,Y).$$

But by (10.92)

$$TG'(u_0 - u*_0 + X, u_1 - u*_1 + Y) = (X,Y).$$

Hence

$$\begin{cases} X(u^\alpha_0 - 1) + Yu^\beta_0 = u_0 - u*_0, \\ X u^\alpha_1 + Y(u^\beta_1 - 1) = u_1 - u*_1. \end{cases} \tag{10.97}$$

Substituting the values of u^α_0, u^α_1, u^β_0 and u^β_1 and solving for X and Y, we find

$$X = \text{correction to } u_0 = \frac{a(2a+5)}{a+2}(u_0 - u*_0) - \frac{2a(a+1)}{a+2}(u_1 - u*_1),$$

$$Y = \text{correction to } u_1 = \frac{2a(a^2 + 2a - 1)}{(a+1)(a+2)}(u_0 - u*_0) - \frac{a(2a-1)}{a+2}(u_1 - u*_1),$$

$$\tag{10.98}$$

which are equivalent to equations (5.37).